PRESERVED COACHING STOCK OF BRITISH RAILWAYS

PART TWO - PRE-NATIONALISATION STOCK

FIRST EDITION

Peter Hall & Peter Fox

Published by Platform 5 Publishing Ltd., Wyvern House, Sark Road, Sheffield S2 4HG, England.

Printed in England by Walker & Carson, Wreakes Lane, Dronfield, Sheffield S18 6PN

ISBN 1-872524-86-9.

GWR Collett standard corridor brake composite No. 6562 built 1938 in service on the Severn Valley Railway at Bewdley on 20th August 1986. The coach is carrying the typical Great Western Railway-style roofboards.
M.A. King

CONTENTS

Front Cover Photograph: GWR Collett inspection saloon (dia. Q.13) No. 80943 seen at Norchard on the Dean Forest Railway on 14th August 1993. *K. Preston*

Back Cover Photograph: SR Maunsell nondescript open brake No. 4432 (dia. 2354) at Tenterden on the Kent & East Sussex Railway on 6th August 1995. *Brian Morrison*

INTRODUCTION

We have just passed through the third significant period of change to have a pronounced effect on railway coaching stock this century. This first was the grouping in 1923, the second was nationalisation in 1948 and the third is the sale of former British Railways-owned carriages to private companies which has recently been completed. The intention of this book is to cover coaching stock associated with the twenty-five years of the grouping between 1923 and 1948 and still in existence either in preservation or a similar status. Coaching stock of the nationalisation period which is now preserved was covered in part one of this series, whilst it is the intention to cover pre-grouping carriages in a future volume.

Before proceeding further it is worthwhile explaining the ground rules used to decide which vehicles are and are not included within this title. The chronological boundaries for inclusion can be generally stated as being included are carriages constructed by the four grouping companies, Great Western Railway, Southern Railway, London, Midland and Scottish Railway and London and North Eastern Railway and in addition carriages of the Pullman Car Company and Wagons-Lits of the same era used in Great Britain. However the boundaries have been extended to cover carriages to the grouping companies designs produced in the years following nationalisation, until such times as their designs were superseded by British Railways standard designs. Additionally designs in production at the time of the grouping are also generally included, particularly if the design was adopted by a grouping company. In addition it was considered sensible to include all locomotive hauled Pullman cars built prior to nationalisation which still exist in what can be considered complete form rather than including the handful of such cars built prior to 1923 in a future volume of this series. There are however several carriages in existence obeying the above criteria which are not included, these fall into two categories. Firstly there are those still in the ownership of British Rail, its subsidiaries and descendants which can be considered to be in either revenue earning or departmental service on the Railtrack network. Secondly there are those that the author is not aware of and are still extant. It is thought few, if any, exist in this category, with the possible exception of bodies of non-passenger carrying coaching stock in use as sheds etc. Should however readers be aware of any omissions, the author would be pleased to hear of them. A more detailed explanation of what is included in each section is given in the relevant introductory paragraphs.

The order of the book is Pullman Car Company stock, stock of the former 'big four' companies, stock of the Wagon-Lits company then appendices giving other useful information. Where possible passenger carrying coaching stock has been split from non-passenger carrying stock within each section although vagaries of numbering schemes have not always allowed this to be practical.

Information contained about the individual carriages listed herein can be split into two categories, historical and preservation. The historical information has been compiled from extensive research of both published works and notes compiled over many years. It is hoped that this information is as accurate as possible. However over the years much contradictory information has been published and it has often been difficult to establish without doubt the correct situation. Thus before criticising the author for errors in this sphere readers should be sure of their sources of information. Remember that the mind is the best distorter of facts. Obviously however any historical correction or clarification regarding the carriages in this book would be gratefully received. Generally speaking detailed historical information which replicates that in what can be considered the definitive works covering the carriages included here in has been omitted, readers being referred to these recommended texts were appropriate. The preservation information is principally compiled from regularly visiting the various sites mentioned and it is believed that information regarding locations is as up to date as is possible. It should however be emphasised that errors are possible in describing the locations due in the main to two factors. Firstly, although much of what is published regarding preserved coaching stock in enthusiast periodicals is accurate, on occasions, what is published is erroneous due to either poor interpretation of the facts or lack of knowledge leading to inaccurate assumptions by the journalists, it being apparent that many periodicals could be greatly improved by their journalists checking facts before going into print. The result of this is that in a few cases, especially with regard to recent developments which the authors have been unable to physically check, published information could be incorporated in good faith, only for it to be subsequently proved to be inaccurate. Secondly, movements of preserved carriages between sites are taking place on an almost weekly basis and no official lists of transfers exist in this field. Thus if a movement between sites has taken place since the last visits it is possible that the author has not become aware of it, thus the location shown may unknowingly be that where the vehicle was last confirmed as being located rather than where it can currently be found. It is believed however that such occurrences in this book can be counted on the fingers of one hand. The author would of course welcome notification of these occurrences if they do in fact exist.

WITH GRATEFUL THANKS

Although much of this book is the result of considerable study and research of the subject by the author over many years it would not have been possible without the help of many others. Thus, the author whilst accepting the bouquets and reluctantly the brickbats for this tome would like to give credit for the assistance given by several people in particular.

Firstly I would like to thank David Morris for his computing consultancy and confusion in bringing much of the information contained here in into electronic format, also for his chauffeuring over many years. Thanks also to Peter Gardner and his occasional substitute Graham Copeland for their navigation on many trips, this having added greatly to the mileage covered in researching this book, also to Graham Dawson for dealing with public relations in often awkward circumstances.

Much assistance has been given by the professionals in carriage restoration and operation whom have freely given of their limited time to resolve queries. Special thanks being due to Charles Paget (The Riviera Ltd), Richard Gibbon (National Railway Museum), Neil Tyhas (Lancastrian Carriage & Wagon), Tim Robbins (Venice Simplon Orient Express), Richard Edmondson (Queen of Scots Train) and Ray Etkin (formerly of the Carriage & Traction Company Ltd).

Several carriage restorers and enthusiasts have been invaluable in providing information both from correspondence and personal contact. In particular I would like to thank Andrew Barclay, Murray Brown, Charlie Cross, Brian Cuttell, Roger Harris, Martin Lear (Cardiff & Avonside Railway Society), John Lloyd, Richard Oakley, David Rouse, Lee Taylor, Clive Warneford, Dave Whittaker, Roger Williams, and Terry Bye the latter in particular for his knowledge of Pullman matters.

Finally thanks to Roger Butcher for the help given in the departmental field which has led to the resolving of many a query and to all those I have forgotten to mention but whose help has been very much appreciated.

THE CURRENT PRESERVATION SCENE

When future railway historians reflect on the preservation phenomena of the second half of the twentieth century, their analysis, I feel sure, will show that, with the exception of post nationalisation designs, coaching stock missed out. The problem being, particularly in respect of passenger carrying carriages included herein, that by the late 1960s, when preservation really began to take off, the majority of pre nationalisation design passenger carrying vehicles had been scrapped. The majority that did survive in British Rail service by this time having been converted to departmental use. It is true that even as late as 1972 a considerable number of LNER Buffet/Restaurants and LMS Sleeping Cars were still in regular daily use and continued so for several years but that was it and even some of these useful LNER Buffet/Restaurants were scrapped rather than being snapped up by preservationists. Fortunately some of the earlier schemes were able to obtain a few vehicles direct from service in the 1960s, generally of later designs, but that was about it for carriages taken into preservation in what could be considered near original condition.

The preservation movement was however given one last opportunity to obtain sound grouping carriages, although these were not necessarily in original condition. An opportunity preservationists surprisingly did not make the most of. In 1979 the Department of Transport decided that the mobile control trains which had up to that time been secret would be disbanded and the vehicles disposed of. The history of mobile control trains dates back to 1953 when planning for the eventuality of any future hostilities included the moving of the district control offices and the construction of replacement static but moveable emergency control centres. Four years later the first train for the Western Region was converted, the scheme then being put on hold. In 1961 the idea was resurrected and eleven further mobile control trains were converted. In total forty eight grouping carriages were converted for the scheme. These trains were generally kept under cover and were regularly maintained so as they could be available for movement at short notice. Regrettably twelve of these carriages were scrapped at the time with twenty six being preserved. Ten were retained by British Rail for other purposes, subsequently three of these have been scrapped, four preserved and three remain in departmental service. Further details of those preserved are given in the introductory paragraphs to the various sections of this book and a full listing of the fleet is given in an appendix.

Otherwise the preservation movement has since the late 1960s been dependent on acquiring carriages which have seen the ravages of departmental service and it will be noted that the majority of passenger carrying carriages included here in have seen such use. The problem here of course for would be restorers is that much of the interior is likely to have been removed and that remaining may well be in a rather dilapidated condition. Although seeming no hopers can be restored to pristine condition, the cost both financially and in man hours is proving beyond the current scope of many preservation sites and many of the carriages included here will be found tarpaulined over (if they are lucky) in sidings slowly deteriorating. In a few cases a more realistic view has been taken by preservationists with obvious no hopers being broken up to provide resources for restoration projects with greater chance of success. Despite considerable criticism, in particular from the commercial enthusiast press, it is expected that further historical carriages will be broken up over the next few years. The argument that preservation is for the foreseeable future being not applicable in the case of railway rolling stock. The reality is that preservation is for so long as people are willing to finance a particular vehicle. When finance ceases then the vehicles existence is best to cease rather than it enduring increased dilapidation prior to the inevitable. This may seem to be a rather cavalier attitude but it is reality, the preservation scene in the authors opinion would have been better served if many former departmental carriages had never been bought and the money directed to those with greater potential. Indeed the last couple of years have seen this taking place at the state subsidised National Railway Museum, it can therefore be considered that even preservation by the state does not ensure immorality when the money is not available.

All is not gloom however as it is possible to travel in superbly restored grouping carriages headed by steam locomotives on a few of Britain's preserved railways giving an experience of a bygone era. In addition a few restored carriages from the grouping era may be found on display at museums around the country. These carriages being a tribute to those whom have dedicated a considerable amount of time and effort to there restoration.

Many of the non-passenger carrying types associated with the grouping era survived much longer than their passenger carrying brethren. The final items not being retired from capital stock by British Rail until the mid 1980s. This has resulted in these being preserved in some numbers and even many of those transferred to departmental service have remained virtually intact. The initial use of many of these vehicles in preservation was for storage and similar purposes, however the increasing demand, particularly from photographers, for restored non-passenger trains has resulted in many of these vehicles being restored for such use. Within their ranks however are included some very historic and interesting vehicles a very few of which have been restored and put on public display.

Particularly on some recent visits by the author to check the whereabouts of carriages at the various preservation sites it is particularly noted that the epidemic of health and safety paranoia is increasingly spreading. One of the consequences of this is that those whom visit such places to view the supposedly historical collection of rolling stock find themselves being increasingly disappointed. Carriages enthusiasts often suffer more so in this respect, with access to view being increasingly restricted. At the same time the same railways continue to appeal to enthusiasts in particular, for funds to restore carriages which the same enthusiasts are refused access to view. Surely it is ironic that it is easier to view carriages in the countries of the former eastern bloc than it is in Britain's so called railway museums. One consequence of this seemingly uncontrollable health and safety epidemic is that the author has been increasingly made less welcome at many sights on recent visits. Is this what the enthusiasts who have willingly contributed to preservation in the past had in mind or does commercialism now rule and gricers are as much a nuisance on private railways as they have been to generations of British Railways shed masters?

Allied to the above point is what the author considers to be the neglect shown to producing accurate stock books by many of the preservation sites. Some very good stock books have been produced which appeal to both enthusiast and normal alike, regrettably few are currently available. The author has over many years built up a reasonable collection of such stock books many of which have been referred to in the compilation of this book particularly in order to establish preservation information. Thus if owners feel they are not accurately reflected in this respect it is suggested that before criticising they revue the quality and availability of information they publish regarding their vehicles.

MAIN LINE RUNNING

The use of preserved carriages from the grouping era on the mainline has had its ups and downs over the years. Readers may remember with some nostalgia the days of rakes of Great Western Railway Carriages operating on the main line in the 1970s along with a good sprinkling of LMS and LNER carriages. Stricter regulations and an intransigence of British Rail during the 1980s and early 1990s has resulted in a situation where in mid 1996 only a very few carriages from the grouping era are used regularly on the main line.

The majority of these however are Pullman Cars included in the 'Venice-Simplon Orient Express' set. Currently five cars from the grouping era are so included along with three later vehicles and two multiple unit vehicles used as hauled stock. These though have all had considerable modification to bring them in line with modern operating practises.

Two other grouping era vehicles are also currently passed for main line use, both being saloons normally used in the formation of luxury trains. The lavish 'Royal Scotsman' train includes the LNER General Managers Saloon, again considerably modified, in its formation. GWR first class saloon 9004 based at Carnforth and used by Railfilms Ltd. is available for attachment to special trains and sees regular use.

It is to be hoped that as the new era progresses a more rational approach will exist within Railtrack allowing other vehicles from the grouping era to return to the main line.

GUIDE TO THE LAYOUT

The layout of information regarding the individually preserved vehicles included in this book generally follows the style established in part one and is hopefully almost self explanatory. Thus it is hoped that readers will not find it necessary to continually refer back to these notes for explanations of the information included.

As previously stated the order of the book is, Pullman Car Company , Great Western Railway, Southern Railway, London, Midland and Scottish Railway, London and North Eastern Railway and Wagon Lits with were possible stock being divided into passenger carrying and non-passenger carrying. This main part of the book is followed by various pages giving additional information regarding carriages and locations. Were possible within each section or sub-section carriages are arranged numerically by a consistent numbering scheme, generally this is the one applicable at nationalisation. In some cases it has been found, due to lack of consistent numbering schemes, to have been necessary to list vehicles chronologically. Details of a particular vehicle or vehicles are given as a main heading along with type code. This is followed by details of the particular lot or lots and the vehicles preserved within them.

Lot details given include the lot number, diagram number, time of construction, principal dimensions, builder, design were appropriate and seating/accommodation, along with any other relevant information. Although this probably makes perfect sense to the majority of readers the following notes are given as added explanation.

Type Code

This is a standard code adopted for the identification of coaching stock. Although there was some slight variation between companies a consistent form is adopted here loosely based on the British Rail system with some pre nationalisation codes incorporated for clarity. With a few exceptions the codes consist of up to four letters and those used in this book are given below:

Note: Unless otherwise stated the code is applicable to bogied vehicles only and vehicles are mounted on four-wheeled bogies.

AT	Auto-Trailer
B	Passenger Brake, Non-gangwayed
BC	Composite Brake, Non-gangwayed
BCK	Corridor Brake Composite
BFK	Corridor Brake First
BG	Passenger Brake, Gangwayed
BG	Passenger Brake, Gangwayed (with shelves for pigeon traffic)
BGZ	Passenger Brake, Gangwayed (six-wheeled)
BM	Milk Brake Van, Non-gangwayed (four-wheeled)
BT	Brake Third, Non-gangwayed
BTK	Corridor Brake Third
BTO	Open Brake Third
BTso	Semi-open Brake Third
BUO	Nondescript Open Brake
BY	Passenger Brake, Non-gangwayed (four-wheeled)
BZ	Passenger Brake, Non-gangwayed (six-wheeled)
CCT	Covered Carriage Truck (four or six-wheeled)
CK	Corridor Composite
CL	Composite with Lavatory, Non-gangwayed
F	First, Non-gangwayed
FISH	Fish Van (four or six-wheeled)
FK	Corridor First
FMV	Fruit and Milk Van (four-wheeled)
FRUIT A	Fruit Van (four-wheeled)
FRUIT B	Fruit Van (four-wheeled)
FRUIT C	Fruit Van (four-wheeled)
FRUIT D	Fruit Van (four-wheeled)
GUV	General Utility Van
HB	Horse Box (four-wheeled)
MCV	Motor Car Van (four-wheeled)
MILK	Milk Tank Wagon (six-wheeled)
MILK FLAT	Milk Trailer Truck (six-wheeled)
PMV	Parcels & Miscellaneous Van (four-wheeled)
POS	Post Office Sorting Van
POT	Post Office Stowage Van
QUAD-ART	Articulated Suburban Quadruplets

RB	Restaurant Buffet (with kitchen)
RLB	Restaurant Buffet Lounge Car (with kitchen or pantry)
RC	Restaurant Composite (with kitchen)
RF	Restaurant First (with kitchen)
RFO	First Class Dining Car
RFso	Semi-open First Class Dining Car
RK	Kitchen Car
RT	Restaurant Third (with kitchen or pantry)
RTO	Third Class Dining Car
SCV	Special Cattle Van (four-wheeled)
SIPHON G	Gangwayed Milk Van
SLF	First Class Sleeping Car
SLT	Third Class Sleeping Car (four berth)
SLT(C)	Third Class Sleeping Car (convertible)
SLT(T)	Third Class Sleeping Car (twin berth)
T	Third (non-corridor)
TK	Corridor Third
TO	Open Third
TST	Theatrical Scenery Truck
UO	Nondescript Saloon

Lot Number/Order Number. The lot number or order number is as the name implies a number given to a particular order placed for rolling stock. In some cases, particularly where stock was constructed by outside contractors numbers appear not to have been issued.

Diagram. This refers to the diagram or layout plan that the vehicle was constructed to. Readers wishing to consult these are referred to the texts recommended in this book, the majority of which have reproduced these drawings.

Built. This is the year or years in which vehicles built to a particular lot were constructed.

Builder. This is the location at which the vehicle was constructed. In many cases just a geographical location is shown, this being a workshop of the appropriate railway company. In other cases an outside contractor has been responsible and in these cases abbreviated details are given of the contractor. Explanation of these abbreviations and the location of their workshops are given opposite. Where two builders are shown the first was responsible for the underframe, the second for the body work.

Design. Particularly in respect of passenger carrying types the design of particular vehicles represents a particular style of construction. Where applicable the style of design is shown.

Dimensions. The dimensions of each lot are given in imperial units with the length followed by the width. All lengths quoted are exclusive of buffers or drawgear.

Seats. This only applies to passenger carrying coaches with seated accommodation and is the amount and type of seats in the carriage when built. 'F' designates first class seats, 'T' designates third class seats. Second class vehicles were also in operation on Southern Railway (later Southern Region boat train routes, but on 3rd June 1956 second class was abolished and third class was redesignated second class. In more recent years it has been redesignated as standard class. 'U' designates unclassified accommodation, i.e. that not specifically designated for the use of first or third class passengers and certain railways referred to unclassified vehicles as 'nondescript'.

Details then follow of any other particular distinctive features regarding that lot of vehicles along with other relevant information. This is then followed by information regarding changes made to the carriages in that particular lot along with any other relevant information regarding their main line career. Details then follow of the individual vehicles.

NUMBERING

Following the vehicle's first number any subsequent capital stock numbers are given, followed by any departmental numbers. This is followed by the location of the vehicle and any other relevant information concerning its current status such as plated number, current number if not previously carried and certain other details which may be of interest to readers.

Renumbering

Many of the vehicles included in this book have carried more than one capital stock number. Generally this has been due to the owning companies introducing revised numbering systems although in a few cases this has been due to the vehicle concerned being modified. Further details of the numbering systems of the grouping companies are given in the introductory paragraphs to each section.

Departmental Numbers

When a carriage is transferred into departmental service it is normally allocated a new number. The majority of vehicles included here which have seen departmental use have been numbered in the various regional series which were used between nationalisation and the 1970s. The Western Region numbered vehicles in the DW150xxx series, the Southern Region in the DS70xxx series, the London Midland Region in the DM39xxxx series and the Eastern Region in the DE32xxxx series. In addition a few vehicles were numbered in short lived numbering schemes, particularly on the Southern Region. In 1966 British Railways introduced the DB97xxxx series, the intention being that all service vehicles converted from condemned coaching stock would be so numbered. Until the 1970s this series was however little used with vehicles continuing to be numbered in the regional series. Several vehicles included in this book have however carried DB97xxxx numbers when in departmental service.

When TOPS was first implemented in 1973 each departmental vehicle acquired a prefix indicating the department which owned it. No prefix indicated that it was a CCE vehicle. A was used for the CM&EE, C for BREL, K for S&T Engineer, L for CM&EE Electrical Construction, P for Shipping and Internal Services, R for Research, T for Traffic, X for Stores and Z for PRO & Publicity. Were the prefix is known to have been applied it is included in this book. Certain vehicles when transferred to departmental service are designated as 'Internal Use Only' such vehicles being given a number in the 0xxxxx series, this indicating that movement is restricted. 02xxxx numbers were issued by the London Midland Region, 04xxxx numbers by the Eastern Region, 06xxxx & 07xxxx numbers by the Western Region, 08xxxx numbers by the Southern Region and 09xxxx numbers by the Scottish Region. It should be noted that a few preserved vehicles have carried more than one departmental identity and in such cases these are shown in chronological order. Departmental numbers shown with an asterisk were allocated but the number was never physically carried.

Location

The location where the carriage is normally to be found is given if known. Fuller details of UK locations including O.S. grid references are given under 'List of Locations'. It should however be noted that it is the intention of this book to record where individual carriages are rather than who owns them, thus it should not be assumed that a vehicle has any obligation to the site were it is located. In certain cases where carriages are located away from the site shown, such as for restoration, details are given of the current temporary whereabouts.

Plated number

Privately owned carriages authorised to run on the Railtrack network are allocated a private owner number and referred to as 'plated'. The number consists of an owner prefix followed by a five figure number in the 99xxx series. Carriages have to be passed by Railtrack each year and this is denoted by a white equilateral triangle painted on the solebar with the year painted in black. Plated carriages spend considerable time away from the location shown for them, thus it should not necessarily be assumed that such carriages will be seen on a visit to the location shown for them. The plated number is only shown for those carriages which are plated at the time of going to press however many other carriages included here have been plated and are allocated private owner numbers. Full details of all such carriages can be found in an appendix towards the rear of this book.

At the time of going to press Railtrack was in the process of reviewing the numbering policy for 'plated' carriages. This will result in BR design vehicles carrying former capital stock numbers rather than numbers in the 99xxx series where their use is in passenger trains. No decision has been taken regarding numbering of 'plated' carriages included in this book, however it is understood Pullman Cars will regain their schedule numbers whilst other vehicles will carry either their original numbers or 99xxx numbers which ever is most practical.

Finally it should be noted that the above explained presentation of information varies slightly for certain carriages due to their individuality. However, the above explanations equally apply.

CONTRACTORS

The following list gives the abbreviations use for contractors who were builders of carriages detailed in this book.

BRCW	Birmingham Railway Carriage and Wagon Company, Smethwick, Birmingham
Clayton	Clayton Wagons, Lincoln
Cravens	Cravens Ltd., Darnall, Sheffield
GRCW	Gloucester Railway Carriage and Wagon Company, Gloucester
Metro	Metropolitan Carriage and Wagon Company, Washwood Heath, Birmingham (later known as Metropolitan Cammell)
Midland	Midland Carriage and Wagon Company
Pullman Car Co.	Pullman Car Company, Longhedge works, Battersea, London

1. PULLMAN CAR COMPANY STOCK

1.0. INTRODUCTION

Unlike with other sections of this book the author does not feel able to recommend further reading for those interested in the 'nuts and bolts' of the individual Pullman cars, it being considered that such a book still remains to be written. However several more general texts covering Pullman cars which give a good appraisal of Pullman operations and contain considerable amounts of more general information regarding the individual cars are thoroughly recommended. These being:-

Pullman in Europe/Behrend, George.- London: Ian Allan, 1962

Pullman: The Pullman car company - its services, cars, and traditions/Morel, Julian.- Newton Abbot: David & Charles,1983

Pullman: travelling in style/Haresnape, Brian.-London: Ian Allan, 1987

Pullman cars on the Southern 1875-1972/Kidner, R.W.-Oxford: Oakwood Press,1987

The layout of information in this section generally conforms with that outlined in 'Guide to Layout', there are however a few additional points to note. Type codes were not generally used for Pullman Cars. Thus in this section they have not been used. It is however possible to comprehend the type of car from the class headings.

Cars described as 'kitchen' contain a kitchen in addition to passenger accommodation.

Cars described as 'brake' contain a compartment for the use of the guard and a luggage compartment in addition to passenger accommodation.

Cars described as 'parlour' consist entirely of passenger accommodation.

Cars described as 'guard' are parlour cars with a brake control and tip-up seat in one end-vestibule, the doors of which are lettered 'GUARD'.

Pullman cars were not generally numbered as such although many did carry numbers, each carrying a title instead, this normally being a name for first class cars and number for third class cars. The final title carried whilst in normal service is given in the following, details of other identities carried normally being given in the notes in the heading. In 1918 however a scheme of schedule numbers was introduced for cars then in existence, this scheme continuing until the demise of the Pullman Car Company as a separate entity in 1962. Over the years this listing did however develop various anomalies and in 1960 it was fully revised. In this section therefore the order of listing is by the 1960 schedule number which is given followed by the final title of the car. Many cars saw use as post war Camping Coaches following withdrawal, details of the numbers allocated being given in the heading for those no longer used as such and after the current location for those still used as such. Numbers suffixed CC were allocated by the Eastern Region of British Railways, numbers suffixed P were allocated by the Southern Region of British Railways, whilst numbers in the 022xxx series were allocated by the London Midland Region and numbers in the 98xx series were allocated by the Western Region.

Although this book is principally concerned with the grouping era it seems prudent to include details of all earlier locomotive-hauled Pullman cars which remain in what can be considered complete condition. Thus details are included of cars built from 1910-1922 which still exist on bogies. A number of other Pullman car bodies also exist from these and early years principally in use as holiday chalets. Thus the obvious commencement of this books coverage is 1907. It was in this year that financier Davison Alexander Dalziel (1854-1927) purchased the British Pullman Car Company running it as a private company. On 30th September 1915 a public company, The Pullman Car Company Ltd, was formed which took over Dalziel's private company although he remained as chairman. The company remained independent throughout the grouping era and also escaped nationalisation in 1948, signing a fifteen year contract with the new administration. In 1954 the British Transport Commission purchased all the ordinary shares thus giving it a controlling interest in the company. The remaining preference shares were subsequently acquired in late 1962 with the Pullman Car Company being absorbed on 31st December 1962 on the expiry of its fifteen year contract. Details of post war locomotive hauled cars and pre war electric multiple unit cars are excluded from this book, details are however given in the following Platform 5 books:

Preserved coaching stock of British Railways: part one - BR design stock/Hall, Peter & Fox, Peter.-Shefield: Platform 5, 1994

Preserved locomotives of British Railways/Hall, Peter & Fox., Peter.-ninth edition.-Sheffield: Platform 5,1995

Five cars remain from the 1907-1915 period. 'EMERALD' and 'SAPPHIRE' are the oldest cars being constructed in 1910 for use on the South Eastern & Chatham Railway 'Continental Express' service between London Charing Cross and Dover. Cars usually worked in pairs on this service with a parlour car matched to a kitchen car, fortunately the two survivors are representative of these two designs although the later has subsequently been rebuilt. 'EMERALD', a kitchen car, was burnt out in 1955 and subsequently became instruction Car 101. It now having been cosmetically restored at the Conwy Valley Railway Museum. 'SAPPHIRE', a parlour car rebuilt as a kitchen car, however has in recent years seen considerable restoration work taking place on it and now forms luxury dining accommodation at the Pullman Lodge Hotel on the sea front at Seaburn. 'ALICANTE' is a 1912 Cravens of Sheffield built car, it was built initially for services on the South Eastern & Chatham Railway between London and Folkestone. This car was one of many converted to camping coaches in the early 1960s and along with several similarly converted cars remains to this day at Marazion faced with an uncertain future. 'MIMOSA' and 'TOPAZ' both date from 1914, the former being one of the cars now at Marazion whilst 'TOPAZ' is fully restored and is on continuous display at the National Railway Museum.

The years from 1915 until the grouping in 1923 saw the construction of a considerable number of new cars along with various rebuilds. The most notable survivors from this period are the five cars with six wheel bogies. The first of these 'CAMBRIA' was built in 1920 for the Great Eastern Railway 'Hook Continental' service from London to Harwich. When built this was a kitchen car, however in 1924 it was rebuilt as a brake at the Pullman car company Longhedge works. It owes its survival to the fact that it became a departmental carriage in around 1938. Forty years later it was rescued from Beighton near Sheffield and now awaits restoration at the Kent & East Sussex Railway. Six new six-wheeled bogie cars were delivered to the South Eastern & Chatham Railway in 1921, as with earlier cars they were intended to run as pairs with a kitchen and parlour car running together. Three of these have survived and again, as with the 1910 cars, examples of each have been preserved. Of the survivors 'Car No. 99' and 'ROSALIND' are located with 1910 car 'SAPPHIRE' well away from their original sphere of activity at the Pullman Lodge Hotel, Seaburn. The other survivor is 'Car No. 97' which is another of the cars at Marazion. The fifth survivor, 'Malaga', spent the whole of its operating life in the South of England before being rescued by Ian Allan Ltd in 1962, it now forming part of their Shepperton office complex.

Post war shortages meant many materials were in short supply, this resulted in the construction of a number of cars on the underframes of redundant wartime built hospital ambulance coaches. The other five surviving cars from this period were all built on the underframes of London & North Western Railway hospital ambulance carriages. All five were built as kitchen cars, however they were all altered during their service lives. Three of the survivors became Camping Coaches following withdrawal, two of these 'Car No. 135' and 'Car No. 137' continue with this function at Ravenglass whilst the other 'MAID OF KENT' awaits restoration at Chipping Warden. 'MAID OF KENT' last saw use as a Camping Coach at Heacham on the Kings Lynn to Hunstanton line were it kept company with 'Montana' detailed below. It subsequently saw static departmental use at Kings Lynn were it was used for staff instruction and first aid training. The other two were converted to Observation Saloons in 1947 for use on the 'Devon Belle'. Although 'Car No. 13' continues to see use on the Paignton and Dartmouth Railway the other car has had an eventful subsequent history. 'Car No 14' formed part of Alan Pegler's ill fated 'American Flying Scotsman Tour Train' and was, along with Pullman cars 'Lydia', 'Isle of Thanet' and other carriages in the train left behind in San Francisco when the locomotive was repatriated. 'Car No. 14' was however fortunately retrieved from the dock side and now serves as part of an office/conference complex at "Fortunes Almanac", 150 Chestnut Street, San-Francisco.

A number of cars were constructed in the years following the grouping. Of the earliest of these one complete batch of four built as first brakes survives. 'Car No. 503', 'Car No. 154', 'Car No. 502' and 'MONTANA' saw early use on the London-Dover all Pullman train introduced in 1924 known as the 'Continental Express', This train becoming known as the 'Golden Arrow' in more recent years. All were withdrawn in the early 1960s becoming Camping Coaches. The three converted to thirds survive at Marazion whilst the fourth 'MONTANA' is located at the former Barnwell Junction, Cambridge. Another preserved car which first saw use in the 'Continental Express' was 'FIINGALL' this car having been restored at the Bluebell Railway now forms part of that lines Pullman Dining Train. The Bluebell Railway is also the home of another car from this era, that being 'Car No. 54' which was built as a third class Kitchen but was rebuilt as a third Brake in 1937, this car awaiting restoration. In 1926 a new Pullman service was introduced to serve Hastings, however the restrictions on the route resulted in six cars, all kitchens, being built to the reduced restriction '0' loading gauge of this line. Details of the various Southern Railway restrictions are given in the introductory paragraphs to that section. Two of these cars survive, 'THEODORA' and 'BARBARA', both on the Kent & East Sussex Railway. 'BARBARA' has been fully restored and sees use on the lines wine and dine trains. Also entering service on the Southern Railway in 1926 was Parlour Third 'Car No. 36', this being one of the cars refurbished in 1951 for the 'Golden Arrow'. It now resides on the Colne Valley Railway being used for dining purposes.

Three cars survive from those introduced to LNER Pullman services in 1927. 'LEONA' has for several years provided laviish accommodation for diners at the 'Orient Express' restaurant close to Elsenham station. Regrettably this establishment has recently closed and 'LEONA', which lacks bogies and running gear is likely to be relocated in the near future. The remains of 'HEBE' had until recently been incorporated in a cafeteria contained within Hyper-Hyper, a department store located at 26 Kensington High Street, West London. Following closure on 31st August 1996, the remains of 'HEBE' were removed to the Bluebell Railway where they will be used as a source of spares in the restoration of other Pullman Cars. The third 'MINERVA' is now formed as part of the 'Venice-Simplon Orient Express' set, being the oldest car in the formation. Both 'Leona' and 'Minerva' were amongst cars refurbished for use on the post war 'Golden Arrow'. Also from this era is 'Car No. 64', this was originally allocated to the LNER for use on the London-Harwich Boat Trains were it was used as a dining car. It was rebuilt by the Pullman Car Company at Preston Park in 1937 as a Parlour Third. For many years this car was located at Hereford having been part of the erstwhile Bulmers Cider train. It now however is used as part of the Bluebell Railways Pullman dining train.

A significant development came about in 1928 when all steel construction was adopted. This followed the disastrous accident near Sevenoaks of 24th August the previous year which highlighted the hazard of wooden bodied stock when it was involved in an accident. The first all steel cars consisted of a batch of twenty four cars for the London & North Eastern Railway 'Queen of Scots' trains. Seven of these cars still exist now seeing a variety of uses. 'Car No. 75' and 'URSULA' have for many years now seen use as a static restaurant behind the Spot Gate public house at Mier Heath. 'AGATHA' and 'LUCILLE' are with the Venice-Simplon Orient express although only 'LUCILLE' has been fully restored to main line standards, 'Agatha' still awaiting full restoration. 'Car No. 76' was also until recently awaiting restoration as part of the Venice Simplon Orient express but has recently been loaned to the Bluebell Railway were it is to be restored for use in the lines Pullman dining train. At the time of publication movement to the Bluebell Railway was imminent. 'Car No. 79' has recently entered service on the North Yorkshire Moors Railway dining train following a prolonged restoration whilst 'PHYLLIS' languishes in a field following its removal from the Ashford Steam Centre on that venture's demise.

'Ibis' has an interesting pedigree, being one of ten cars built in 1925 for CIWL whom used them on their Milan-Nice service. They were bought back from CIWL in 1928 and rebuilt by the Midland Carriage and Wagon Company. It now forms part of the 'Venice-Simplon Orient Express' set.

In 1929 a new Pullman service was introduced on the Great Western Railway between London and Plymouth Millbay Docks, named 'Ocean Liner Express', which ran in connection with the sailings of trans Atlantic liners. For this service seven cars were constructed by the Metropolitan Carriage & Wagon Company. Two of these cars, 'ZENA' and 'IONE', survive in the formation of the Venice-Simplon Orient Express.

The final two surviving cars date from 1931 being two Parlour Thirds built for use on LNER Pullman trains. 'Car No. 83' was another car originally preserved at Hereford as part of the Bulmers train before passing to its present owners were it awaits its call. 'Car No. 84' has spent all its preservation life on the Keighley & Worth Valley Railway.

When compared with other sections of this book it will be realised that Pullman Cars have faired far better than other stock in terms of preservation. Few of the cars listed in this section are lying in a semi-derelict condition tarpaulined over in a remote siding. Obviously the grandeur of the Pullman name has helped in this respect with its appeal to a much wider spectre of the population, emphasised by the success of the 'Venice Simplon Orient Express' operation.

1.1. PULLMAN CAR STOCK LIST

PULLMAN KITCHEN FIRST

Built: 1910 **Builder:** BRCW **Dimensions:** 57'6" x 8'7½" **Seats:** 16F

EMERALD: Seating remodelled from 19F to 16F in 1924. Converted to Instruction Carriage in 1955. SAPPHIRE: Rebuilt from Parlour First with 24F seats in 1924. Converted to Camping Coach P51 in 1960.

32	EMERALD	Conwy Valley Railway Museum	Instruction car 101
43	SAPPHIRE	Pullman Lodge Hotel & Restaurant,Seaburn	Used as Restaurant

Built: 1912 **Builder:** Cravens **Dimensions:** 57'6" x 8'7½" **Seats:** 19F

Rebuilt as composite in 1935 seating 12F 14T. Damaged by fire in 1949 and rebuilt as kitchen first. Converted to camping coach in 1962.

47	ALICANTE	The Old Marazion Station Holiday Centre	Camping coach 9874

Built: 1914 **Builder:** BRCW **Dimensions:** 57'6" x 8'7½" **Seats:** 19F

Rebuilt as composite in 1935 seating 12F,14T. Damaged by fire in 1949 and rebuilt as kitchen first. Converted to camping coach in 1962.

50	MIMOSA	The Old Marazion Station Holiday Centre	Camping coach 9869

PULLMAN PARLOUR FIRST

Built: 1914 **Builder:** BRCW **Dimensions:** 57'6" x 8'7½" **Seats:** 24F

59	TOPAZ	National Railway Museum	

PULLMAN KITCHEN FIRST

Built: 1921 **Builder:** Pullman Car Co. **Dimensions:** 63'6" x 8'7" **Seats:** 16F

6-wheeled bogies.

92	MALAGA	Ian Allan Ltd., Shepperton	Used as boardroom

PULLMAN PARLOUR THIRD

Built: 1921 **Builder:** BRCW **Dimensions:** 63'6" x 8'7" **Seats:** 26T

6-wheeled bogies. Declassified in 1947 from parlour first 'CALAIS'. Converted to camping coach in 1962.

97	CAR No. 97	The Old Marazion Station Holiday Centre	Camping coach 9870

PULLMAN GUARD THIRD

Built: 1920 **Builder:** BRCW **Dimensions:** 63'6" x 8'7" **Seats:** 26T

6-wheeled bogies. Rebuilt from kitchen first 'PADUA' in 1946 by Pullman Car Company, Preston Park Works, Brighton. Converted to camping coach P59 in 1962. In 1971 taken into departmental service as a civil engineers staff coach numbered DW150431.

99	CAR No. 99	Pullman Lodge Hotel & Restaurant,Seaburn	Used as Restaurant

PULLMAN KITCHEN FIRST

Built: 1921 **Builder:** BRCW **Dimensions:** 63'6" x 8'7" **Seats:** 16F

6-wheeled bogies. Converted to camping coach P47 in 1960. In 1971 taken into departmental service as a civil engineers staff coach numbered DW150430.

102	ROSALIND	Pullman Lodge Hotel & Restaurant,Seaburn	Used as Restaurant

PULLMAN OBSERVATION CAR

Built: 1921 **Builder:** Pullman Car Co. **Dimensions:** 58'6" x 8'7" **Seats:** 27F

Built on underframes of LNWR ambulance coaches as kitchen first seating 47F. Converted to bar cars in 1937 at Pullman Car Company, Preston Park Works. Rebuilt 1947 at Pullman Car Company, Preston Park Works to Pullman observation cars.

113 CAR No. 13 Paignton & Dartmouth Railway 'DEVON BELLE'
114 CAR No. 14 Fortunes Almanac, 150 Chestnut Street, San-Francisco, CA, USA

PULLMAN BRAKE FIRST

Built: 1920 **Builder:** Clayton **Dimensions:** 63'8½" x 8'9" **Seats:** 21F

6-wheeled bogies. Rebuilt from kitchen first in 1924 by Pullman Car Company, Longhedge Works. Converted to Staff & Tool Van 960820 in 1938.

119 CAMBRIA Kent & East Sussex Railway DE960820

PULLMAN KITCHEN THIRD

Built: 1921 **Builder:** Clayton **Dimensions:** 58'6" x 8'6" **Seats:** 19T

Built on underframe of LNWR ambulance coach as kitchen first ELMIRA. Converted to kitchen composite in 1933 at Pullman Car Company, Preston Park Works & to kitchen third as "CAR No. 135" in 1948. Converted to camping coach in 1960.

135 CAR No. 135 Ravenglass & Eskdale Railway Camping coach 022261

PULLMAN KITCHEN FIRST

Built: 1921 **Builder:** Clayton **Dimensions:** 58'6" x 8'6" **Seats:** 19F

Built on underframe of LNWR ambulance coach as kitchen first 'FORMOSA', rebuilt as kitchen composite at Pullman Car Company, Preston Park Works in 1934 seating 12F 16T. Rebuilt back to kitchen first and re-named 'MAID OF KENT'in 1948 to replace original car of that name which had been declassified (Schedule No. 137 below). Converted to camping coach in 1960.

136 MAID OF KENT Great Central Railway (Southern Division) Camping coach CC161

PULLMAN KITCHEN THIRD

Built: 1921 **Builder:** Clayton **Dimensions:** 58'6" x 8'6" **Seats:** 19T

Built on underframe of LNWR ambulance coach as kitchen first 'MAID OF KENT', rebuilt as kitchen composite at Pullman Car Company, Preston Park Works in 1934 & to kitchen third in 1948. Converted to camping coach in 1960.

137 CAR No. 137 Ravenglass & Eskdale Railway Camping coach 022262

PULLMAN BRAKE THIRD

Built: 1923 **Builder:** BRCW **Dimensions:** 57'6" x 8'7½" **Seats:** 26T

Built as brake firsts AURORA, FLORA and JUNO. Converted to brake thirds 1946–52 and renumbered to Car Nos. 503, 154 and 502. Converted to camping coaches in 1962.

153 CAR No. 503 The Old Marazion Station Holiday Centre Camping coach 9873
154 CAR No. 154 The Old Marazion Station Holiday Centre Camping coach 9871
155 CAR No. 502 The Old Marazion Station Holiday Centre Camping coach 9872

PULLMAN BRAKE FIRST

Built: 1923 **Builder:** BRCW **Dimensions:** 57'6" x 8'7½" **Seats:** 26F

Converted to camping coach in 1962.

156 MONTANA Barnwell Junction, Cambridge Camping coach CC165

PULLMAN BRAKE THIRD

Built: 1923 **Builder:** Clayton **Dimensions:** 63'10" x 8'7" **Seats:** 33T

Rebuilt from kitchen third in 1937 seating 39T at Pullman Car Company, Preston Park Works.

157 CAR No. 54 Bluebell Railway

PULLMAN KITCHEN FIRST

Built: 1925 **Builder:** BRCW **Dimensions:** 63'10" x 8'7" **Seats:** 22F

175 FINGALL Bluebell Railway

Built: 1926 **Builder:** Metro **Dimensions:** 57'1½" x 8'1" **Seats:** 17F

Built to Tonbridge – Battle line loading gauge (restriction 'O'). Originally seated 20F, remodelled as Composite seating 12F 11T in 1932, remodelled back to First in 1946. Painted green in 1958 and labelled 'Buffet Car' for use on Southampton Boat Trains. Sold to British Rail in 1960 and numbered 7864 & 7867 respectively.

184 THEODORA Kent & East Sussex Railway
185 BARBARA Kent & East Sussex Railway

PULLMAN PARLOUR THIRD

Built: 1926 **Builder:** BRCW **Dimensions:** 63'10" x 8'7" **Seats:** 42T

Originally seated 54T but reduced in 1946. Refurbished 1951 for use in the 'Golden Arrow'.

194 CAR No. 36 Colne Valley Railway 'HERMIONE'

PULLMAN GUARD THIRD

Built: 1927 **Builder:** Midland **Dimensions:** 63'10" x 8'7" **Seats:** 36T

Built as Parlour First seating 26F 'LEONA'. Rebuilt at Pullman Car Company, Preston Park in 1947 as a guard third, subsequently used on the 'Golden Arrow'.

208 CAR No. 208 Orient Express Restaurant, Elsenham Body only remains

PULLMAN KITCHEN FIRST

Built: 1927 **Builder:** Metro. **Dimensions:** 63'10" x 8'7" **Seats:** 22F

Built as kitchen first 'MARCELLE', converted to kitchen third 'Car No 105' in 1946, converted back to kitchen first 'HEBE' in 1962.

210 HEBE Bluebell Railway – now scrapped – Part of body remains

PULLMAN GUARD FIRST

Built: 1927 **Builder:** Midland **Dimensions:** 63'10" x 8'7" **Seats:** 26F

Built as parlour first. Rebuilt at Pullman Car Company, Preston Park in 1951 as a guard first for use on the 'Golden Arrow'. Restored as Parlour First.

213 MINERVA Venice-Simplon Orient Express VSOE99535 'VSOE' set

PULLMAN PARLOUR THIRD

Built: 1928 **Builder:** Midland **Dimensions:** 63'10" x 8'7" **Seats:** 42T

Originally a second class dining car. Rebuilt as Pullman Car by Pullman Car Company, Preston Park in 1937.

219 CAR No. 64 Bluebell Railway 'CHRISTINE'

Built: 1928 **Builder:** Metro. **Dimensions:** 63'10" x 8'7" **Seats:** 42T

228 CAR No. 75 The Spot Gate, Mier Heath Used as Restaurant
229 CAR No. 76 Bluebell Railway 'EVE'

PULLMAN BRAKE THIRD

Built: 1928 **Builder:** Metro. **Dimensions:** 63'10" x 8'7" **Seats:** 30T

232 CAR No. 79 North Yorkshire Moors Railway

PULLMAN KITCHEN FIRST

Built: 1928 **Builder:** Metro. **Dimensions:** 63'10" x 8'7" **Seats:** 20F

238	PHYLLIS	Great Bower Farm, Molash	

PULLMAN PARLOUR FIRST

Built: 1928 **Builder:** Metro. **Dimensions:** 63'10" x 8'7" **Seats:** 24F

239	AGATHA	Venice-Simplon Orient Express	Not identifiable
242	URSULA	The Spot Gate, Mier Heath	Used as Restaurant
243	LUCILLE	Venice-Simplon Orient Express	VSOE99541 'VSOE' set

PULLMAN KITCHEN FIRST

Built: 1925 **Builder:** BRCW **Dimensions:** 63'10" x 8'7" **Seats:** 20F

Built for CIWL, Italy (CIWL 52 & 55). Returned to UK in 1928 and rebuilt by Midland Carriage & Wagon Company.

245	IBIS	Venice-Simplon Orient Express	VSOE99534 'VSOE' set
246	LYDIA	National Railroad Museum, Green Bay, Wisconsin, USA	

PULLMAN GUARD FIRST

Built: 1925 **Builder:** Metro. **Dimensions:** 63'10" x 8'7" **Seats:** 24F

Built as a parlour first for CIWL, Italy and named 'LEONA'(CIWL 53). Returned to UK in 1928 and rebuilt by BRCW and named 'PRINCESS ELIZABETH'. Rebuilt as guard first by Pullman Car Company, Preston Park in 1950.

247	ISLE OF THANET	National Railroad Museum, Green Bay, Wisconsin, USA	

PULLMAN PARLOUR FIRST

Built: 1928 **Builder:** Metro. **Dimensions:** 63'10" x 8'7" **Seats:** 24F

254	ZENA	Venice-Simplon Orient Express	VSOE99536 'VSOE' set

PULLMAN KITCHEN FIRST

Built: 1928 **Builder:** Metro. **Dimensions:** 63'10" x 8'7" **Seats:** 20F

255	IONE	Venice-Simplon Orient Express	VSOE99539 'VSOE' set

PULLMAN PARLOUR THIRD

Built: 1931 **Builder:** BRCW **Dimensions:** 63'10" x 8'7" **Seats:** 42T

261	CAR No. 83	Venice-Simplon Orient Express	'PRINIA'
262	CAR No. 84	Keighley & Worth Valley Railway	'MARY'

2. GREAT WESTERN RAILWAY STOCK

2.0. INTRODUCTION

Of the grouping companies the Great Western Railway was the only one which was essentially an existing company. Therefore rather than considering coaching stock built from 1923 as is generally the case for the other grouping companies the start date has been taken as the Churchward era which commenced in 1902. Thus included here are all preserved carriages to the designs of Churchward, Collet and Hawksworth.

Considering the following for all things Great Western the author has had particular difficulties in tracing comprehensive historical information on the non-passenger carrying types in particular. However recommended for further information regarding the passenger carrying types included herein is:-

Great Western Coaches:1890-1954./Michael Harris.- Newton Abbot: David & Charles, 1966.

Logical numbering schemes were used by the Great Western Railway but the system became rather confused over a period of time with blocks of numbers sometimes being reused for new stock. Passenger-carrying types are listed generally in numerical order, but for clarity have been split into three sections i.e. auto-trailers, ordinary passenger stock and saloons, sleeping & catering cars. Non passenger carrying types are treated similarly. For these four separate numbering schemes existed for Passenger full brakes and Post Office Vehicles, Carriage Trucks, Livestock Vehicles and Pershables Vehicles. Each numbering scheme is considered separately with preserved vehicles listed numerically within each.

The Great Western Railway/British Railways Western Region Camping Coach number series eventually covered the range 9869-9999 and a substantial number of the preserved carriages saw such use. In this section Camping Coach numbers are given following the capital stock number. It should however be noted that several Camping Coaches subsequently saw departmental service.

Ten Great Western Railway carriages were included in the mobile control trains mentioned earlier, these comprised seven collett design passenger carrying carriages and three Siphon Gs which were converted to generator vans. Regrettably one of the Siphon Gs has been scrapped but the other nine vehicles have been preserved. The two western region control trains were kept for the majority of there time in a locked shed at Craven Arms station.

2.0.1. PASSENGER CARRYING COACHING STOCK

2.0.1.1. Churchward Stock

Auto Trailers

To reduce operating costs the concept of a small engine unit and coachwork as one vehicle was taken by Britain's railways from around 1900. Most proved underpowered and unreliable, but the GWR evolved a competent design and came to operate the largest fleet of steam railcars. Following on from this in 1905 the GWR developed its version of the autotrain, with a conventional locomotive pushing or pulling anything up to four trailers. From 1915-36 the steam railcars were progressively rebuilt as auto-trailers or withdrawn.

38 is one of the short 59′ 6″ trailers, of which six were built in 1907. It sees occasional passenger use at its current home of the Telford Railway Centre, a task it has undertaken for many years. 92 is of 70′ length with a gangway connection fitted at the non-driving end. Along with 212 it awaits restoration at Didcot. 212 was originally steam railmotor 93 built in 1908, this was one of the last seven Railmotors rebuilt as a trailer, conversion not taking place until 1936. Conversion involved little more than the use of the space vacated by the redundant engine unit for extra seating and guard's and luggage compartment.

Dreadnought Coaches

Churchward's 'Dreadnought' coaches were a truly revolutionary design being the first to adopt elliptical roofs. For the time they were truly massive with bodies of 69′ length and 9′ 6″ width. Interior design was also revolutionary, the side corridor stock had no exterior doors to the compartment side, entry and exit being by way of the large end and central vestibules. In addition, the internal corridors crossed from one side to the other, divided by the central vestibule. The only coach of this design to survive is Corridor Third 3299. When built this was gas lit rather than electric as was the case with the majority of those built. Progress on the restoration of this coach continues as time permits at Didcot.

Toplight Stock

Following the 'Dreadnoughts' the GWR moved to a more conventional design of elliptical-roofed coach which were built from 1907-1922. These were known as 'Toplights' on account of the oblong hammered glass fanlights above quarter and full-size windows. The majority owe their survival to seeing departmental service or conversion to camping coaches.

The final outpost of traditional Camping Coaches is Dawlish Warren in Devon where until recently nine were located. One has however just been removed leaving eight for the summer 1996 season. Those currently present date from the early 1980s when they replaced nine older camping coaches which had all been converted from 'Toplight' stock. The nine numbered 9878-9886 obviously aroused interest among preservationists with all but 9878 being preserved. Of these all now serve as volunteer accommodation on their respective railways except 9884 which is stored awaiting restoration at the Gloucestershire-Warwickshire Railway. Incidentally 9878 was broken up on site at Exeter in 1980. The other three Camping Coaches on the West Somerset Railway which were converted from 'Toplights', 9887-9889, were located at Blue Anchor until closure by British Rail of the line in 1971. They continue to be used for volunteer accommodation although now located elsewhere on the line. The only other carriage preserved direct from service as a camping coach is 9918 which was originally Corridor Third 2426. This now sees use for volunteer accommodation at Hampton Loade on the Severn Valley Railway. A few camping coaches saw departmental use before final withdrawal, often no actual renumbering took place, with just a departmental prefix being added to the number. For many years three 'Toplight' camping coaches 9875, 9876 & 9921 saw departmental use at St. Austell as S&T Contractor's Staff & Dormitory Coaches along with Collet Corridor Third 4777 also preserved. These four were moved in 1982 to Exeter for use in connection with the resignalling. Regrettably 9921 suffered extensive fire damage and was subsequently scrapped, however the other two camping coaches have now been preserved at the Bodmin Steam Railway.

Most notable amongst the 'Toplights' to have seen departmental service is Brake Corridor Third 2360. In 1931 this coach was selected by the GWR for conversion to a track recording car. It was stripped internally except for the two front compartments and lavatory. Observation windows were placed at the brake end. In the former guard's compartment was fitted equipment which gave arise to the coaches nickname of 'Whitewash Coach'. The whitewash apparatus is directly connected to the bogies and automatically operated by their movement over the track rather than by the general oscillation of both bogies and bodywork. Coming on to a rough stretch of track, the movement of each lurch of the bogies is transmitted by electrical impulses. The primary coil is attached to the bogie bolster, with the field strength kept constant, a secondary coil slides within this primary coil and is activated by the action of the bogie frames. With violent 'hunting' over the stretch of track, the action of the secondary coil generates electrical impulses, transmitted through relays, acting on a solenoid operating a flap valve. Each exceptional lurch is sufficient to open this valve and deposit, through a pipe, about a quart of whitewash over the track while, simultaneously, a horn is sounded in the coach. In the centre of the coach, independent of the whitewash equipment, a standard Hallade track recorder was installed. This maintains a continuous graph of the journey, showing on four separate lines: braking and rolling, lateral movements, alignment and super elevation, vertical movements and the location of each whitewash 'drop'. There was a recessed section of body panelling on each side with a lookout for the operators. Speedometers were fitted at the brake end of the coach. When a test was in progress the on train staff would keep their eyes on the track from this end. This coach continued in use until the 1980s before passing to the National Collection. It was displayed as part of the National Railway Museum on Tour Exhibition held at Swindon in 1990, subsequently it has been stored at York.

The only two 'Toplight' coaches to have been preserved direct from service are the pair of Brake Thirds at Didcot. These coaches were used on City services until 1939 and on other Western Region London suburban workings until 1956/7. In 1958 they were transferred to South Wales for use on miners trains, they remained on these duties with gas lighting in place of electric until late 1964. Both are now stored at Didcot awaiting further restoration.

Much work is required to return the remainder of the preserved 'Toplight' coaches to passenger service although progress is being made with Corridor Third 3930 at the Severn Valley Railway.

Saloons

The oldest of the three saloons preserved is 6479. The underframe of this coach started out with the

Manchester & Milford Railway and carried a composite body. It was withdrawn in 1908. However a couple of years later the bodywork was removed and an Inspection Saloon constructed on the underframe by the GWR. It saw many years service as an Inspection Saloon latterly acquiring number 80977 in the post war Inspection Saloon number series. In preservation it has been generally well looked after although it is looking rather neglected whilst in storage at the Pontypool & Blaenavon Railway. It is not clear whether the Ystwth Valley Railway project will now go ahead, thus a cloud currently hangs over this most historic carriage.

9055 was built as a third class saloon using a standard 57' underframe and bodywork generally conforming to contemporary 'Toplight' stock. The coach has a saloon at each end with a centre side-corridor compartment. This coach has been meticulously restored at the Severn Valley Railway were it sees regular passenger use.

9369 was built for party hire, it has a side corridor giving access to two saloons with inward facing seats, an ordinary compartment, a lavatory and the guard. This coach is again a credit to the Severn Valley Railway were it has been meticulously restored for passenger use.

2.0.1.2. Collett Stock

Auto Trailers

During 1928-36 the remaining Great Western Railway steam railcars were mostly converted to auto-trailers and only 32 new auto-trailers were built. Six from this period have however been preserved. The preserved examples from lot 1394, 163, 167 and 169, are bow ended and of 59' 6'' length. Some restoration has taken place on these three although much still remains to be done. The two built to lot 1410, 174 and 178 are of the longer 62' 8'' bow ended type and both of these are currently undergoing extensive restoration. 190 is similar to the later two but has flush-panelled bodysides. This has been fully restored at Didcot and sees regular use there.

Bow-Ended Stock

The standard passenger stock introduced by the GWR after Grouping was a steel panelled vehicle generally of similar lines to the 'Toplight' stock. The design had a bow-ended body generally 58' 4¼'' over the ends and usually 9' wide. Doors to each compartment were provided on both corridor and compartment sides. All the preserved examples of passenger carrying coaching stock have seen departmental service prior to preservation, consequently none have yet been fully restored. Corridor Third 4777 is of particular interest as for many years it was located at St. Austell and latterly Exeter along with two 'Toplight' coaches also now preserved. Corridor Brake Composite 7976 is the oldest of those preserved and is some what of a cross between 'Toplight' and 'Bow-ended' stock being of 57' length with flatter ends.

Bow-Ended Catering Cars

Six Catering carriages built to Collet's bow ended design have been preserved, all of which have seen departmental use.

The two Restaurant Composites now preserved have had rather different histories in recent years. 9580 had its third class saloon converted to a buffet in 1953 and in 1960 was taken into departmental service as the Western Region S&T Managers Saloon. Following withdrawal it was purchased by Peter Waterman and thoroughly overhauled by Lancastrian Carriage & Wagon. It now sees use as a luxury saloon at the East Lancashire Railway. 9605 was part of a batch of ten built for cross country services with an end kitchen and two saloons with fixed seating. Following withdrawal it was taken into departmental service as a mobile work study office. It was then earmarked for the National Collection and was acquired with this in mind from British Rail in 1978. It was initially stored at Swindon Works and latterly at the Science museum storage facilities at Wroughton airfield. Although some restoration work took place at Wroughton it was found to be in very poor structural condition and in 1994 was deemed surplus by the National Railway Museum. It has subsequently been moved to the Pontypool and Blaenavon railway were it is intended that it will be fully restored as part of the Ystwyth Valley project.

In 1932 the GWR introduced ten dining car twin sets, these composed of a restaurant first with kitchen and a third class dining car. 9615 and 9627 are examples from these twin sets and although they have both seen departmental service both have remained in remarkably near original condition. Both have been extensively restored at the Severn Valley Railway and now see regular use in dining trains. It should also be mentioned that both were also formed in the main line set of Great Western Railway carriages operated by the Severn Valley Railway in the 1970s.

The other two third class dining cars preserved have had a most interesting history. During 1925 the Great Western Railway constructed eight sets of articulated stock for main line use. Each set consisted of one twin and two triple articulated sub sets. One of the triplets was formed of first class dining car, Kitchen car and third class dining car. These articulated sets did not prove particularly successful due to lack of flexibility and the carriages were rebuilt as conventional vehicles in 1936-37. The two preserved third class diners were rebuilt in 1936 and continued in service for another twenty or more years. Following withdrawal both were used with little alteration in the western region mobile control trains, 9653 being formed in the 1958 train and 9654 in the 1962 train. When the trains were disbanded they were taken into the national collection and subsequently loaned to the Severn Valley Railway were they have seen extensive restoration and now are regularly used for dining trains.

First Class Saloons

These two fine coaches were built as first class corridor saloons for private hire. They are bow ended, 61′ 4″ long and 9′ wide with the sides bulging round at the bottomsides. Observation windows are fitted at the body ends. The interior followed the normal layout with saloons at each end, a separate first class compartment and a central kitchen/pantry and lavatory. All saloon interior panelling is in walnut. Both were fitted with new windows in the 1930s and in 1947 lost the separate compartment as well as being modernised internally. In BR days both saw use as saloons for railway officials. 9004 transferred to the North Eastern Region were it was used as the Civil Engineer's saloon numbered DE321011. 9005 stayed on home ground as the Western Region General Managers saloon. The saloons were withdrawn in 1972 and 1974 respectively. 9004 was purchased by Sir William McAlpine whom used it for many years as his personal mainline saloon. 9005 was preserved at Didcot, however no major restoration work took place, it remaining in as withdrawn Blue/Grey livery. 9004 subsequently passed to Nick Dobson whom fully restored it for use as a mainline saloon normally used in connection with the 'Statesman set'. More recently he has also rescued 9005 from Didcot and is currently restoring it to develop further his activities with main line luxury saloons.

Super Saloons

These coaches were among the most famous built by the GWR and deservedly so in view of their handsome outline and high-class Pullman type furnishings. Eight were built for use on the Plymouth-Paddington Ocean Liner expresses, where they replaced Pullman Cars. The 'Super Saloons' are more handsome in appearance than the contemporary Pullman cars and also wider as the extreme width of the 61′ 4″ body is 9′ 7″. As a result, they were subject to some restrictions on route availability and the doorways were recessed at an angle to the bodywork. Prior to 1939 they carried the names shown. The interior furnishings were very lush with walnut panelling and single armchair seats on either side of the gangway. There is also a single compartment at one end, 9118 had this replaced with a kitchen in 1935. After the war they were generally renovated and the large windows received sliding ventilators. The Plymouth boat services were discontinued from the end of 1962, but the 'Super Saloons' continued on special duties as well as making regular appearances on the Newbury Racecourse specials. Of the five preserved all are now either seeing occasional passenger use or in the case of 9111 on public display at their present homes.

Standard Corridor Stock 1933-1936

In 1933 following several years of construction of carriages to the bow ended design the GWR reverted to a flat ended design. This type continued with the traditional layout of an exterior door to each compartment and four doors to the corridor side.

The majority of passenger carrying examples preserved have seen departmental service. Five of these saw use in the western region mobile control trains, Corridor Thirds 5848, 5856 and 5929 in the 1958 train and Corridor Thirds 5813 and 5863 in the 1962 train. Other than externally restored 5856 which is now at the delightfully restored Tintern Parva station in the Wye Valley all the others are at the Dean Forest Railway awaiting the opportunity for restoration work to commence in earnest. Restoration has however been carried out on several of the others with Corridor Brake Third 5883, Corridor Third 5952 and Corridor Brake Composite 6913 all having seen mainline use.

Of particular interest is Restaurant Buffet with Kitchen 9631 also referred to as a 'Quick Lunch Bar Car'. The interior resembled a cocktail bar: there was a pantry at one end and the rest of the interior was made up of a continuous bar counter faced by twelve stand-up bar stools. Show cases and tea urns were placed on the bar counter. The windows behind the bar were of frosted glass, while on the other side there were large windows high placed on the bodyside. Following a long period on loan to the Severn Valley Railway were it could be savoured by passengers it is now on display at the National Railway Museum.

Centenary Stock

In the year of its centenary the GWR built two sets of coaches of an entirely new design for the Cornish Riviera Limited. The 'Centenary' stock, as it became known, took advantage of the old broad gauge loading gauge and the coaches were built to the maximum width of 9' 7'', the bodies being bow-ended and 61' 4¼'' long over the ends. As with the 'Super saloons' the doorways were recessed. For the first time since the 'Dreadnought' stock of 1905 passenger access was via end vestibules only so that large compartment side windows could be used. Enough coaches were built to make up two ten coach sets together with spares for strengthening at holiday periods. The interior decor was restrained with polished wood panelling. Only one vehicle has survived, Restaurant First with Kitchen 9635, which was purchased on withdrawal in 1963. It was modernised in early post war days with new interior furnishings, including low backed bench type seats. It has been located at several sites and is now at Didcot awaiting further restoration.

Standard Corridor Stock 1936-1940

The GWR moved forward to a modern layout for corridor stock in 1936 with entry through end vestibules only, large windows on both corridor and compartment sides and more attractive interiors. The bodies were wooden framed with steel body and roof panelling.

The passenger carrying types preserved have nearly all seen passenger use since preservation. The majority, those with 07915x departmental numbers saw use in the Swindon Works test train prior to preservation and needed little attention, all but 7362 seeing mainline use in the 1970s. Of the remainder only Corridor Brake Third 1649 did not come direct from service and this is the only one requiring extensive restoration.

Excursion Stock 1935-1940

The GWR did not build any centre-gangway open stock for general service, unlike the other grouping companies. The open coaches built from 1935-40 were kept for most of their lives in sets for excursion use. The bodies were of modern appearance with large windows with sliding ventilators. The interiors were in contemporary style with square outlines to seat frames, partition doorways and lightshades. The three preserved Open Thirds are from two sets built in 1937 being 60' long and 9' wide. Each has two saloons with end and centre vestibules. The Open Brake Third was of slightly different dimensions being built in 1940. This being the only one in need of extensive restoration having being used at a scouting centre following withdrawal.

'Sunshine' Stock

This design marked an important step forward in GWR corridor coach practise for standard stock, introducing large windows extending almost to the cantrail on the corridor side, end entrance vestibules and large compartment side windows. The only preserved example is of the later variant which had a standard waistline with the same window and droplight arrangement extending up to the cantrail on the corridor side. When in departmental service 1595 was used as a Civil Engineers Staff and Dormitory coach. It now is one of the many stored carriages owned by the Carriage and Traction Company Ltd. awaiting developments at the Railway Age.

Special Saloons

9001 and 9002 are self contained saloons intended for VIP travel. They have a coupe compartment, day saloon, dining saloon, pantry and kitchen. In the dining saloon, fixed seating was provided but the coupe and main saloon had settees and armchairs with small tables. The original interiors were rather spartan, but were repanelled and refurnished in 1953. 9001 has seen main line use since preservation but is now on static display at the Birmingham Railway Museum.

Royal Saloons

The two Royal saloons were ordered in 1943 but were not constructed until 1945. They were originally intended for use as special saloons and had the same specification as the above special saloons but with the addition of sleeping accommodation. They were initially used as special saloons but were upgraded for the use of royalty in 1948. Use was made of two salvaged underframes from war damaged carriages. 9006 was equipped with two bedrooms, a bathroom, a small end-saloon seating seven on easy chairs and settees, a dining room seating eight, an attendant's sleeping compartment and a fair-sized kitchen, including a refrigerator. 9007 had no catering facilities but a lounge, two large bedrooms for use by the royal travellers, and stowage space, which was in reality the 'guard's compartment'. Observation windows were fitted at the saloon ends. These along with Hawksworth Corridor Brake Composites 7372 and 7377 formed the Western Region Royal train for many years. In 1964 when provision of Royal Trains was centralised, the Corridor Brake Composites were transferred to general use. The huge reduction taking place in the carriage fleet at the time soon saw them being designated surplus. The two saloons passed to the London Midland Region and continued to be used for Royal Train duties, being designated for use by HM Queen Elizabeth the Queen Mother. They were last used in 1979. Following various periods of display at the National Railway Museum the two saloons have been temporarily relocated, 9006 being stored at MoD BAD Kineton and 9007 displayed in the museum at Bishops Lydeard on the West Somerset Railway. Both of the Corridor Brake Composites have also been preserved with 7372 seeing regular use at Didcot and 7377 seeing occasional use on the South Devon Railway.

Inspection Saloons

In 1948 some very ancient inspection saloons still survived. Thus seven purpose built saloons were constructed to replace them. These had the general profile of the standard stock built in the late 1930s and had observation windows at each end. The interior consisted of a saloon at each end and the usual central lavatory and pantry. Warning gongs were fitted at each end and folding steps were provided at each side. All seven have now been preserved in what can be considered restored condition. 80972 was formerly passed for mainline use when based at Birmingham Railway Museum.

The design was continued with some variations by British Rail whom built one Inspection Saloon in 1957 (DB999506) and two in 1960 (DB999508/90) based on these very successful saloons. All three remain in service to this day.

2.0.1.3. Hawksworth Stock

Auto Trailers

In 1951 fifteen new auto train saloons were constructed, the first for over fifteen years. The new saloons had the same slab sided profile as the standard corridor stock, with large bodyside windows and very deep ventilators. Seven of these have been preserved all coming straight from service, the majority seeing regular use in preservation although invariably in the consist of conventional trains.

Standard Corridor Stock

Indicative of the forward looking spirit of the GWR after the war were the Hawksworth designed coaches which embodied many interesting developments and experiments. The stock brought a new profile to the GWR of a slab-sided box with sloping roof ends and the length of 64' allowed for bigger vestibules and larger compartments. Examples of three designs are preserved. Corridor Third, Corridor Brake Third and Corridor Brake Composite. Excluding the previously mentioned Corridor Brake Composites only two Corridor Thirds and a Corridor Brake Third of the passenger carrying carriages came direct from service.

Both of the Corridor Thirds preserved on the Severn Valley have been fully restored having come direct from service. 2119 which saw main line use in the 1970s has been stored awaiting further attention for many years now, however 829 sees regular use and has been immaculately restored. 796 has a special claim to fame however as in 1961 it was withdrawn and rebuilt as a new western region dynamometer car numbered DW150192. It saw over twenty years service in this form eventually being based at the Railway Technical Centre at Derby. It was initially preserved at the Foxfield Railway but subsequently moved to Didcot from where it was active on the main line, usually with locomotive 71000 'Duke of Gloucester'. It has recently moved to Steamtown Railway Centre, Carnforth where its future use is awaited with interest.

In 1967 eighteen of the Hawksworth Corridor Brake Thirds were taken into departmental service and converted to Civil Engineers Staff and Dormitory coaches numbered DW150390-DW150407. Many of these survived in departmental use until the late 1980s and not surprisingly ten of these are now in the hands of the preservation movement. To date none of these ten have been restored and it is expected that several will in turn be broken up as a source of spares for other preserved GWR Hawksworth design carriages. The other preserved Corridor Brake Third, 2202, came straight from service and saw some mainline use in the 1970s, it is now displayed and occasionally used at Didcot.

Sleeping Cars

The only special-duty Hawksworth outline vehicles were the four first class sleeping cars all of which are preserved. These were ten berth cars, with the usual attendant's compartment, and interesting as they were equipped with Stone's pressure ventilation. Interior panelling was in laminated plastic throughout: green and beige in the corridors and ivory in the compartments. A number of other fittings were also plastic, while all the metalwork was in satin-silver finish. They all now see use for volunteer accommodation at their present homes.

2.0.2. PASSENGER FULL BRAKES AND POST OFFICE VEHICLES

These vehicles are generally to passenger-carrying designs which have been described earlier.

Four passenger full brakes built to the Churchward Toplight style have been preserved. All saw service after withdrawal from capital stock. 261 being used for many years in a South Wales Steel Works before being rescued for preservation which is currently taking place. The other three all saw departmental service prior to preservation. 1145 & 1150 on the Severn Valley have been externally restored whilst 1159 awaits attention.

Four vehicles to the Collett bow-ended design are included. Post Office Stowage Van 814 is a direct replacement for the original vehicle of this design and number which was destroyed in 1940 and thus was built much later than other carriages of this design. This, the only GWR Postal Van to be preserved has had quite an interesting history. In 1959 it was displaced from the Great Western TPO and along with Sorting Vans 806, 807, 808, 846, 847 and Stowage Vans 812 & 813 was transferred to the Southern Region. These eight vans remained in use until 1971/72 when they were replaced by vehicles of LMS and BR design. 814 was however then taken into departmental stock as an Enparts Van on the Western Region, being used as such until 1975 when it was taken into preservation at Didcot. It has subsequently been restored to a high standard and sees use on demonstration postal trains. Interestingly Stowage Van 813 was also taken into departmental stock as an ENPARTS van but was subsequently scrapped. The bodies of 807 and 812 still survive at Wessex Traincare Ltd, Eastleigh Works deep in Southern Railway territory. Gangwayed Passenger Brake 1184 is the only preserved example of bow-ended stock not to have seen departmental use and has thus been a much easier restoration project than the others

Six Collett standard passenger full brakes have been preserved. The three from the 1933-1936 period all saw departmental service prior to preservation. 111 saw little alteration however and was quickly restored following arrival at Didcot. 184 & 185 were however used extensively as enparts vans which saw the removal of corridor connections. Restoration is however now well advanced on 185 at the Gloucestershire-Warwickshire Railway and it is now being used as a museum coach, externally the restoration looks most impressive. The three from the later 1936-40 period continued in service until the late 1970s although by that time they had been reduced to general parcels duties with several having had gangways removed. 276 which had had its gangways removed then saw further use as a Breakdown Train tool van before being preserved on the South Devon Railway.

As with the previously mentioned immediate post war Collett design full brakes, the similar Hawksworth design vehicles remained in service until the late 1970s with some seeing further life in departmental service. 295 and 297 are the only preserved examples to retain their gangways, 297 seeing use as a generator and support van for a cinema coach whilst in departmental service.

2.0.3. NON-PASSENGER CARRYING COACHING STOCK

Excluding passenger brakes and Post Office Vehicles which were constructed to match passenger-carrying stock and considered above, the Great Western Railway produced some very distinctive designs of non-passenger coaching stock and two in particular, milk vans and fruit vans being particularly well known. Three separate numbering schemes were used for these vehicles, these being Carriage Trucks, Livestock Vehicles and Perishables Vehicles.

2.0.3.1. Carriage Trucks

Two designs of carriage truck are represented in preservation, these being the four wheeled covered carriage truck known as 'Python' and the bogied General Utility Van known as 'Monster'. Only a few of the 'Monster' vans were constructed over a period of many years, many lasted well into British Rail days, indeed some were actually built by British Railways. The design featured a tall roof profile and end doors. In BR days they were often used as originally envisaged, to convey circus equipment, and this kind of traffic survived into the 1970s. However their main use has been the carriage of vehicles and thus they are eligible for CCT classification although as bogied vehicles they were classified as GUV. All four preserved carriage trucks await full restoration, being currently used for storage purposes at their respective homes.

2.0.3.2. Livestock Vehicles

Only one complete GWR Horse Box survives and this has seen considerable alteration whilst in departmental service. The other two being just bodies which have been acquired following several years of non railway use.

The two preserved Special Cattle Vans date from British Railways days although built to a GWR design.

2.0.3.3. Perishables Vehicles

By the 1930s the majority of milk traffic being conveyed by the railways was being carried in milk tanks. However perhaps because it served a territory within which small scale dairy farming was a major industry, the GWR continued to build vans to cater for milk-churn traffic. The final design produced in any numbers was the Siphon G. These were bogie vehicles fitted with corridor connections and four pairs of outward opening doors per side. Many continued in use until the early 1980s, however by this time they were being used for more general parcels traffic and many had had their gangways removed. Several also saw use as Newspaper Vans during the 1970s, for this they acquired electric heat, preserved examples of these being 1019, 1046 and 1047. Following withdrawal many saw departmental use. Three were used as generator vans in the western region mobile control trains of which two have been preserved. 2775 and 2790 were formed in the six coach 1958 control train, following disbanding 2775 went to the National Railway Museum were it remains stored. 2790 and 2798 from the 1962 train were initially retained by British Rail for possible use as Exhibition train generator vans and were moved to Salisbury with this in mind. This however did not come to fruition and they were subsequently disposed of, 2790 passed to the Dean Forest Railway whilst regrettably 2798 was scrapped. Those taken into departmental service in the 1970s and numbered in the DB975xxx series saw use as vans for the movement of materials between various locations, however in most cases such use was fairly short lived.

The Great Western Railway also constructed a sizeable fleet of Milk Tanks. Eleven of these from various lots have been preserved so far although one has lost its tank. All are six-wheel examples although 2009 preserved at the delightful Mangapp's Farm Railway Museum was rebuilt from a four-wheeler. Also numbered in this series are the Milk Tank Trailer Trucks, these being flat wagons used to convey road milk tank trailers by rail. The preserved example at Didcot has a road trailer mounted on it.

One of the GWR's main parcels traffics was the market garden produce from various locations. The vans provided for this traffic had additional ventilation slats in the sides to allow cool air to circulate. The final design, Fruit D, was constructed from the late 1930's and even adopted by British Railways as a standard design. Three sets of doors were provided on each side all of which had special steps below them to help the loaders climb in and out with ease. The Fruit Ds were not used all the year round on seasonal fruit traffic and at other times were used as ordinary parcels vans. Fruit Ds were particularly popular for departmental conversion, presumably the good access making them ideal for storage and transport of materials. Thus the majority of preserved examples have seen departmental service although the three that did not were amongst the last to be withdrawn from capital stock in the mid 1970s. Several examples of earlier designs of Fruit Vans survive in preservation with Fruit As, Fruit Bs and Fruit Cs being represented all of which saw departmental service.

Fish traffic was also important for the GWR with two designs of van being constructed. Regrettably none of the shorter 21' long vans have been preserved from the thirty-five built. However the more prolific longer 28'6" design of which one hundred and fifty were built is well represented in preservation. The triple sets of doors on these again made them popular for departmental conversion with all preserved examples having seen such use.

2.0.3.4. Freight Stock often Confused with Perishables Vehicles

Also included are details of preserved six-wheel water tanks and Mink D and Mink G vans. Although freight stock these are included due to the similarity of types included here with which they are often confused.

2.1 GWR PASSENGER-CARRYING STOCK

2.1.1. AUTO-TRAILERS

AUTO-TRAILER AT

Lot: 1126 **Built:** 1907 **Builder:** Swindon **Design:** Churchward
Diagram: N **Seats:** 64T **Dimensions:** 59′6″ x 9′0″

38 079022 Telford Railway Centre

Lot: 1198 **Built:** 1912 **Builder:** Swindon **Design:** Churchward
Diagram: U **Seats:** 70T **Dimensions:** 70′0″ x 9′0″

92 Didcot Railway Centre

Lot: 1394 **Built:** 1929 **Builder:** Swindon **Design:** Collett
Diagram: A.27 **Seats:** 64T **Dimensions:** 59′6″ x 9′0″

163 ADW150315 Oswestry Cycle & Railway Museum
167 079050 Dean Forest Railway
169 064749 Gloucestershire-Warwickshire Railway

Lot: 1410 **Built:** 1930 **Builder:** Swindon **Design:** Collett
Diagram: A.28 **Seats:** 64T **Dimensions:** 62′8″ x 9′0″

174 TDW150313 Llangollen Railway
178 Swindon L. C. & W. Works Ltd

Lot: 1480 **Built:** 1933 **Builder:** Swindon **Design:** Collett
Diagram: A.30 **Seats:** 64T **Dimensions:** 62′8″ x 9′0″

190 079052 Didcot Railway Centre

Lot: 1542 **Built:** 1936 **Builder:** Swindon **Design:** Churchward
Diagram: A.26 **Seats:** 77T **Dimensions:** 70′0″ x 9′0″

Rebuild of Railmotor 93, lot 1142, diagram R, built 1908.

212 Didcot Railway Centre

Lot: 1736 **Built:** 1951 **Builder:** Swindon **Design:** Hawksworth
Diagram: A.38 **Seats:** 64T **Dimensions:** 64′0″ x 8′11″

225 South Devon Railway
228 South Devon Railway
231 Didcot Railway Centre
232 Paignton & Dartmouth Railway

Lot: 1766 **Built:** 1954 **Builder:** Swindon **Design:** Hawksworth
Diagram: A.43 **Seats:** 64T **Dimensions:** 64′0″ x 8′11″

238 Paignton & Dartmouth Railway
240 South Devon Railway

2.1.2. ORDINARY PASSENGER STOCK

CORRIDOR THIRD TK

Lot: 1623 **Built:** 1940 **Builder:** Swindon **Design:** Collett
Diagram: C.77 **Seats:** 64T **Dimensions:** 60′11½″ x 8′11″ **Type:** Standard

536 079152 Didcot Railway Centre

OPEN BRAKE THIRD BTO

Lot: 1644 **Built:** 1940 **Builder:** Swindon **Design:** Collett
Diagram: D.130 **Seats:** 40T **Dimensions:** 60′11½″ x 8′11″ **Type:** Excursion stock

650 Severn Valley Railway Body only remains at Foley Park

CORRIDOR THIRD — TK

Lot: 1691 **Built:** 1948 **Builder:** Swindon **Design:** Hawksworth
Diagram: C.82 **Seats:** 64T **Dimensions:** 64'0" x 8'11" **Type:** Standard

796 was rebuilt as a Dynamometer Car in 1961.

796	ADW150192	Steamtown Railway Museum, Carnforth
829		Severn Valley Railway

Lot: 1593 **Built:** 1938 **Builder:** Swindon **Design:** Collett
Diagram: C.77 **Seats:** 64T **Dimensions:** 60'11½" x 8'11" **Type:** Standard

1086	079154	Severn Valley Railway
1087	079158	Severn Valley Railway
1111	079159	Didcot Railway Centre
1116	079157	Severn Valley Railway
1146	079153	Severn Valley Railway

OPEN THIRD — TO

Lot: 1575 **Built:** 1937 **Builder:** Swindon **Design:** Collett
Diagram: C.74 **Seats:** 64T **Dimensions:** 60' x 9'0" **Type:** Excursion stock

1285		South Devon Railway
1289		Didcot Railway Centre
1295		South Devon Railway

CORRIDOR BRAKE THIRD — BTK

Lot: 1574 **Built:** 1937 **Builder:** Swindon **Design:** Collett
Diagram: D.124 **Seats:** 32T **Dimensions:** 60'11¼" x 8'11" **Type:** Sunshine stock

1595	DW150359	Carriage & Traction Company Ltd Stored at Crewe Carriage Shed

Lot: 1594 **Built:** 1938 **Builder:** Swindon **Design:** Collett
Diagram: D.127 **Seats:** 32T **Dimensions:** 60'11½" x 8'11" **Type:** Standard

1649	079170	Dean Forest Railway

CORRIDOR THIRD — TK

Lot: 1720 **Built:** 1949 **Builder:** Swindon **Design:** Hawksworth
Diagram: C.82 **Seats:** 64T **Dimensions:** 64'0" x 8'11" **Type:** Standard

2119		Severn Valley Railway

CORRIDOR BRAKE THIRD — BTK

Lot: 1732 **Built:** 1950 **Builder:** Swindon **Design:** Hawksworth
Diagram: D.133 **Seats:** 32T **Dimensions:** 64'0" x 8'11" **Type:** Standard

2148	DW150403	Severn Valley Railway
2180	DW150405	West Somerset Railway
2196	DW150395	Carriage & Traction Company Ltd Stored at Crewe Carriage Shed
2202		Didcot Railway Centre
2214	DW150393	Severn Valley Railway
2216	DW150402	Llangollen Railway
2218	DW150400	Severn Valley Railway
2225	DW150392	Cholsey & Wallingford Railway
2232	DW150397	Gloucestershire-Warwickshire Railway
2233	DW150401	Severn Valley Railway

Lot: 1744 **Built:** 1951 **Builder:** Swindon **Design:** Hawksworth
Diagram: D.133 **Seats:** 32T **Dimensions:** 64'0" x 8'11" **Type:** Standard

2242	DW150391	Buckinghamshire Railway Centre

Lot: 1174 **Built:** 1911 **Builder:** Swindon **Design:** Churchward
Diagram: D.46 **Seats:** 32T **Dimensions:** 56'0" x 9'0" **Type:** Toplight

Rebuilt as a Track recording Car in 1931.

2360 DW139 National Railway Museum 'Whitewash Coach'

Lot: 1180 **Built:** 1911 **Builder:** Swindon **Design:** Churchward
Diagram: D.47 **Seats:** 32T **Dimensions:** 57'0'' x 9'0'' **Type:** Toplight

2370 ADW309 Swindon L. C. & W. Works Ltd

CORRIDOR THIRD TK

Lot: 1167 **Built:** 1910 **Builder:** Swindon **Design:** Churchward
Diagram: C.30 **Seats:** 64T **Dimensions:** 56'0'' x 9'0'' **Type:** Toplight

2426 CAMPING COACH 9918 Severn Valley Railway
2434 DW150038 Bodmin Steam Railway

Lot: 1172 **Built:** 1911 **Builder:** Swindon **Design:** Churchward
Diagram: C.31 **Seats:** 64T **Dimensions:** 57'0'' x 9'0'' **Type:** Toplight

2447 ADW150019 Swindon L. C. & W. Works Ltd

Lot: 1234 **Built:** 1914 **Builder:** Swindon **Design:** Churchward
Diagram: C.32 **Seats:** 64T **Dimensions:** 56'11¼'' x 8'11¼'' **Type:** Toplight

2573 CAMPING COACH 9879 West Somerset Railway 'CAROL'
2578 CAMPING COACH 9889 West Somerset Railway

Lot: 1098 **Built:** 1905 **Builder:** Swindon **Design:** Churchward
Diagram: C.24 **Seats:** 72T **Dimensions:** 69'0'' x 9'6'' **Type:** Dreadnought.

3299 079002 Didcot Railway Centre

Lot: 1286 **Built:** 1921 **Builder:** Swindon **Design:** Churchward
Diagram: C.32 **Seats:** 64T **Dimensions:** 56'11¼'' x 9'0'' **Type:** Toplight

Rebuild of 3939, lot 1246 built 1915.

3631 CAMPING COACH 9880 South Devon Railway 'FLORENCE'

Lot: 1289 **Built:** 1921 **Builder:** Swindon **Design:** Churchward
Diagram: C.31 **Seats:** 64T **Dimensions:** 57'0'' x 9'0'' **Type:** Toplight

Rebuild of 24xx, lot 11xx built 1910.

3639 CAMPING COACH 9887 West Somerset Railway

Lot: 1292 **Built:** 1921 **Builder:** Swindon **Design:** Churchward
Diagram: C.31 **Seats:** 64T **Dimensions:** 57'0'' x 9'0'' **Type:** Toplight

Rebuild of 3xxx, lot 12xx built 1917.

3655 Didcot Railway Centre

Underframe only remains. Used for GWR 580.

Lot: 1295 **Built:** 1921 **Builder:** Swindon **Design:** Churchward
Diagram: C.35 **Seats:** 64T **Dimensions:** 57'0'' x 8'11¾'' **Type:** Toplight

Rebuild of 3xxx, lot 12xx built 1917.

3665 CAMPING COACH 9886 South Devon Railway 'BERYL'

Lot: 1313 **Built:** 1922 **Builder:** Swindon **Design:** Churchward
Diagram: C.35 **Seats:** 64T **Dimensions:** 57'0'' x 9'0'' **Type:** Toplight

Rebuild of 3xxx, lot 12xx built 1917.

3668 CAMPING COACH 9888 West Somerset Railway

BRAKE THIRD (non-gangwayed) BT

Lot: 1275 **Built:** 1921 **Builder:** Swindon **Design:** Churchward
Diagram: D.62 **Seats:** 60T **Dimensions:** 48'0'' x 8'5¼'' **Type:** Toplight

3755 Didcot Railway Centre
3756 Didcot Railway Centre

CORRIDOR THIRD — TK

Lot: 1269 **Built:** 1920 **Builder:** Swindon **Design:** Churchward

Diagram: C.32 **Seats:** 64T **Dimensions:** 56′11¼″ x 8′11¼″ **Type:** Toplight

3885	3385	CAMPING COACH 9882	West Somerset Railway	'HILDA'
3898		CAMPING COACH 9884	Gloucestershire-Warwickshire Railway	'FREDA'

Lot: 1246 **Built:** 1915 **Builder:** Swindon **Design:** Churchward

Diagram: C.32 **Seats:** 64T **Dimensions:** 56′11¼″ x 8′11¼″ **Type:** Toplight

3917		CAMPING COACH 9883	Llangollen Railway	Numbered 3719 'GRACE'
3930	DW150011		Severn Valley Railway	

Lot: 1256 **Built:** 1919 **Builder:** Swindon **Design:** Churchward

Diagram: C.35 **Seats:** 64T **Dimensions:** 56′11¼″ x 8′11¼″ **Type:** Toplight

3950	CAMPING COACH 9876	060905	Bodmin Steam Railway	
3951	CAMPING COACH 9875	060904	Bodmin Steam Railway	
3963	CAMPING COACH 9885		Llangollen Railway	'ALICE'
3980	CAMPING COACH 9881		West Somerset Railway	'ELSIE'

Lot: 1352 **Built:** 1925 **Builder:** Swindon **Design:** Collett

Diagram: C.54 **Seats:** 64T **Dimensions:** 58′4½″ x 9′0″ **Type:** Bow ended

4546	KDW150205	060903	Severn Valley Railway
4553	KDW150207		Didcot Railway Centre

Lot: 1369 **Built:** 1926 **Builder:** Swindon **Design:** Collett

Diagram: C.54 **Seats:** 64T **Dimensions:** 58′4½″ x 9′0″ **Type:** Bow ended

4777	KDW150206	060907	Blackland Railway, Dykes Farm, Blackland
4786	KDW150208		Severn Valley Railway

Lot: 1372 **Built:** 1927 **Builder:** Swindon **Design:** Collett

Diagram: C.54 **Seats:** 64T **Dimensions:** 58′4½″ x 9′0″ **Type:** Bow ended

4872	KDW150209	Severn Valley Railway

Lot: 1374 **Built:** 1927 **Builder:** Swindon **Design:** Collett

Diagram: C.54 **Seats:** 64T **Dimensions:** 58′4½″ x 9′0″ **Type:** Bow ended

4886	DW150201	Severn Valley RailwayOnly Body Remains, Cut in two at Bewdley

Lot: 1383 **Built:** 1928 **Builder:** Swindon **Design:** Collett

Diagram: C.54 **Seats:** 64T **Dimensions:** 58′4½″ x 9′0″ **Type:** Bow ended

5043	ADW150301	Severn Valley Railway
5085	KDW150200	Didcot Railway Centre

CORRIDOR BRAKE THIRD — BTK

Lot: 1384 **Built:** 1928 **Builder:** Swindon **Design:** Collett

Diagram: D.95 **Seats:** 32T **Dimensions:** 58′4½″ x 9′0″ **Type:** Bow ended

5102	DW150234	Northampton & Lamport Railway
5131	DW150246	Bodmin Steam Railway

BRAKE THIRD (non-gangwayed) — BT

Lot: 1493 **Built:** 1934 **Builder:** Swindon **Design:** Collett

Diagram: D.117 **Seats:** 50T **Dimensions:** 57′0″ x 9′0″ **Type:** Standard

5500	071343	Pontypool & Blaenavon Railway

Lot: 1392 **Built:** 1928 **Builder:** Swindon **Design:** Collett

Diagram: D.101 **Seats:** 50T **Dimensions:** 58′2″ x 9′0″ **Type:** Bow ended

5539	DW150328	Pontypool & Blaenavon Railway

CORRIDOR BRAKE THIRD — BTK

Lot: 1490 **Built:** 1933 **Builder:** Swindon **Design:** Collett
Diagram: D.116 **Seats:** 32T **Dimensions:** 57'0'' x 9'0'' **Type:** Standard

5787 079089 Didcot Railway Centre

Lot: 1510 **Built:** 1934 **Builder:** Swindon **Design:** Collett
Diagram: D.118 **Seats:** 32T **Dimensions:** 57'0'' x 9'0'' **Type:** Standard

Formed in Ambulance Train 34 (1943–1946).

5804 3406 ADW150304 Severn Valley Railway

CORRIDOR THIRD — TK

Lot: 1509 **Built:** 1935 **Builder:** Swindon **Design:** Collett
Diagram: C.67 **Seats:** 64T **Dimensions:** 57'0'' x 9'0'' **Type:** Standard

5813 TDW150324 Dean Forest Railway
5848 TDW150029 Dean Forest Railway
5856 TDW150031 Tintern Parva Station Museum
5863 TDW150325 Dean Forest Railway

CORRIDOR BRAKE THIRD — BTK

Lot: 1514 **Built:** 1934 **Builder:** Swindon **Design:** Collett
Diagram: D.118 **Seats:** 32T **Dimensions:** 57'0'' x 9'0'' **Type:** Standard

5883 079135 Severn Valley Railway

CORRIDOR THIRD — TK

Lot: 1527 **Built:** 1935 **Builder:** Swindon **Design:** Collett
Diagram: C.67 **Seats:** 64T **Dimensions:** 57'0'' x 9'0'' **Type:** Standard

5929 TDW150030 Dean Forest Railway
5952 Didcot Railway Centre

CORRIDOR COMPOSITE — CK

Lot: 1382 **Built:** 1928 **Builder:** Swindon **Design:** Collett
Diagram: E.132 **Seats:** 24F 24T **Dimensions:** 58'4½'' x 9'0'' **Type:** Bow ended

6045 DW150293 Severn Valley Railway

CORRIDOR BRAKE COMPOSITE — BCK

Lot: 1350 **Built:** 1926 **Builder:** Swindon **Design:** Collett
Diagram: E.128 **Seats:** 12F 32T **Dimensions:** 58'4½'' x 9'0'' **Type:** Bow ended

6515 KDW150270 South Devon Railway

Lot: 1589 **Built:** 1938 **Builder:** Swindon **Design:** Collett
Diagram: E.159 **Seats:** 12F 32T **Dimensions:** 60'11½'' x 8'11'' **Type:** Standard

6562 Severn Valley Railway
6705 Steamtown National Historic Site, Scranton, PA, USA

Lot: 1508 **Built:** 1934 **Builder:** Swindon **Design:** Collett
Diagram: E.148 **Seats:** 12F 32T **Dimensions:** 57'0'' x 9'0'' **Type:** Standard

6912 079133 West Somerset Railway U/f only remains. Used for GWR 242.
6913 079134 Severn Valley Railway

CORRIDOR COMPOSITE — CK

Lot: 1639 **Built:** 1941 **Builder:** Swindon **Design:** Collett
Diagram: E.162 **Seats:** 24F 24T **Dimensions:** 59'10'' x 8'11'' **Type:** Standard

7284 079156 Severn Valley Railway

7285 Didcot Railway Centre

Lot: 1621 **Built:** 1940 **Builder:** Swindon **Design:** Collett
Diagram: E.158 **Seats:** 24F 24T **Dimensions:** 59'10'' x 8'11'' **Type:** Standard

7313 079155 Didcot Railway Centre

CORRIDOR BRAKE COMPOSITE BCK

Lot: 1640 **Built:** 1941 **Builder:** Swindon **Design:** Collett
Diagram: E.159 **Seats:** 12F 32T **Dimensions:** 60'11½'' x 8'11'' **Type:** Standard

7362 079151 Swindon & Cricklade Railway
7371 Didcot Railway Centre

Lot: 1690 **Built:** 1948 **Builder:** Swindon **Design:** Hawksworth
Diagram: E.164 **Seats:** 12F 32T **Dimensions:** 64'0'' x 8'11'' **Type:** Standard

Royal Train Coaches.

7372 Didcot Railway Centre
7377 South Devon Railway

Lot: 1138 **Built:** 1907 **Builder:** Swindon **Design:** Churchward
Diagram: E.83 **Seats:** 12F 32T **Dimensions:** 57'0'' x 9'0'' **Type:** Toplight

Originally Brake Corridor Tri-Composite seating 12F,12S,16T.

7538 DW150020 Chinnor & Princes Risborough Railway
7545 KDW7545 079076 Swindon & Cricklade Railway

CORRIDOR COMPOSITE CK

Lot: 1171 **Built:** 1911 **Builder:** Swindon **Design:** Churchward
Diagram: E.88 **Seats:** 24F 24T **Dimensions:** 57'0'' x 9'0'' **Type:** Toplight

7740 KDW317 West Somerset Railway

CORRIDOR BRAKE COMPOSITE BCK

Lot: 1323 **Built:** 1923 **Builder:** Swindon **Design:** Collett
Diagram: E.114 **Seats:** 12F 32T **Dimensions:** 57'0'' x 8'6'' **Type:** Bow ended

7976 079027 Didcot Railway Centre

2.1.3. SALOONS, SLEEPING AND CATERING CARS

INSPECTION SALOON

Lot: 1170 **Built:** 1910 **Builder:** Swindon **Design:** Churchward
Diagram: Q.1 **Seats:** 12U **Dimensions:** 43'6'' x 8'0¾''

Built on underframe of Manchester & Milford Railway Composite 149, GWR 7900.

6479 80977 Pontypool & Blaenavon Railway Stored for Ystwth Valley Railway

SPECIAL SALOON

Lot: 1626 **Built:** 1940 **Builder:** Swindon **Design:** Collett
Diagram: G.62 **Dimensions:** 60'11¼'' x 8'11''

6-wheel bogies. Two built.

9001 Birmingham Railway Museum
9002 Didcot Railway Centre

FIRST CLASS SALOON

Lot: 1431 **Built:** 1930 **Builder:** Swindon **Design:** Collett
Diagram: G.59 **Dimensions:** 61'4½'' x 9'0''

Two built.

9004 DE321011 Steamtown Railway Centre, Carnforth RFM99053
9005 Steamtown Railway Centre, Carnforth

ROYAL SALOON

Lot: 1673 **Built:** 1945 **Builder:** Swindon **Design:** Collett
Diagram: G.64 **Dimensions:** 60'11¼" x 8'11"

6-wheel bogies. Built on underframe of 1133, lot 1593, diagram C.77 built 1938.

9006 National Railway Museum Stored at MoD BAD Kineton

Lot: 1673 **Built:** 1945 **Builder:** Swindon **Design:** Collett
Diagram: G.65 **Dimensions:** 60'11¼" x 8'11" **Type:** Royal saloon

6-wheel bogies. Built on underframe of 1598, lot 1574, diagram D.124 built 1937.

9007 West Somerset Railway National Collection

FIRST CLASS SALOON

Lot: 1209 **Built:** 1912 **Builder:** Swindon **Design:** Churchward
Diagram: G.43 **Seats:** 50F **Dimensions:** 57'0" x 9'0"

9055 DW150127 Severn Valley Railway

FIRST CLASS SLEEPING CAR SLF

Lot: 1702 **Built:** 1951 **Builder:** Swindon **Design:** Hawksworth
Diagram: J.18 **Berths:** 10 **Dimensions:** 64'0" x 8'11"

6-wheel bogies. Four built.

9082 Severn Valley Railway
9083 Didcot Railway Centre
9084 Severn Valley Railway
9085 Severn Valley Railway

THIRD CLASS SALOON

Lot: 1400 **Built:** 1929 **Builder:** Swindon **Design:** Collett
Diagram: G.58 **Seats:** 44T **Dimensions:** 58'4½" x 9'0" **Type:** Bow ended

9103 079124 Severn Valley Railway

FIRST CLASS SALOON

Lot: 1471 **Built:** 1932 **Builder:** Swindon **Design:** Collett
Diagram: G.60 **Seats:** 29F **Dimensions:** 61'4½" x 9'7" **Type:** Super saloon

9111 South Devon Railway 'KING GEORGE'
9112 Didcot Railway Centre 'QUEEN MARY'

Lot: 1471 **Built:** 1932 **Builder:** Swindon **Design:** Collett
Diagram: G.61 **Seats:** 29F **Dimensions:** 61'4½" x 9'7" **Type:** Super saloon

9118 rebuilt with a Kitchen (dia. H.51).

9113 Didcot Railway Centre 'PRINCE OF WALES'
9116 Paignton & Dartmouth Railway 'DUCHESS OF YORK'
9118 Didcot Railway Centre 'PRINCESS ELIZABETH'

NONDESCRIPT SALOON

Lot: 1250 **Built:** 1923 **Builder:** Swindon **Design:** Churchward
Diagram: G.56 **Seats:** 44U **Dimensions:** 56'11¾" x 8'11¾"

9369 DW150128 Severn Valley Railway

RESTAURANT COMPOSITE (with KITCHEN) RC

Lot: 1349 **Built:** 1925 **Builder:** Swindon **Design:** Collett
Diagram: H.33 **Seats:** 12F 24T **Dimensions:** 58'4½" x 9'0" **Type:** Bow ended
This vehicle has a centre kitchen.

9580 KDW150266 East Lancashire Railway

Lot: 1451 **Built:** 1930 **Builder:** Swindon **Design:** Collett
Diagram: H.38 **Seats:** 18F 23T **Dimensions:** 61'4½" x 9'0" **Type:** Bow ended
This vehicle has a kitchen at one end.

9605 TDW150330 Pontypool & Blaenavon Railway

This vehicle is stored for Ystwyth Valley Railway.

RESTAURANT FIRST (with KITCHEN) RF

Lot: 1468 **Built:** 1932 **Builder:** Swindon **Design:** Collett
Diagram: H.39 **Seats:** 23F **Dimensions:** 61'4½" x 9'3" **Type:** Bow ended
This vehicle has a kitchen at one end.

9615 DW150336 Severn Valley Railway

THIRD CLASS DINING CAR RTO

Lot: 1469 **Built:** 1932 **Builder:** Swindon **Design:** Collett
Diagram: H.40 **Seats:** 63T **Dimensions:** 61'4½" x 9'3" **Type:** Bow ended
This vehicle has no kitchen.

9627 079112 Severn Valley Railway

Lot: 1359 **Built:** 1925 **Builder:** Swindon **Design:** Collett
Diagram: H.51 **Seats:** 63T **Dimensions:** 50'6¾" x 9'0" **Type:** Bow ended

Built as articulated stock. 9653 is a rebuild of 10020, diagram H.32. 9654 is a rebuild of 10036, diagram H.32. No kitchen.

9653 TDW150032 Severn Valley Railway National Collection
9654 TDW150326 Severn Valley Railway National Collection

RESTAURANT BUFFET (with Kitchen) RB

Lot: 1518 **Built:** 1934 **Builder:** Swindon **Design:** Collett
Diagram: H.41 **Seats:** 12U **Dimensions:** 57'0" x 9'0" **Type:** Standard

'Quick Lunch Bar Car'.

9631 National Railway Museum

RESTAURANT FIRST (with KITCHEN) RF

Lot: 1540 **Built:** 1935 **Builder:** Swindon **Design:** Collett
Diagram: H.43 **Seats:** 24F **Dimensions:** 61'4½" x 9'7" **Type:** Centenary

9635 Didcot Railway Centre

INSPECTION SALOON

Lot: 1701 **Built:** 1948 **Builder:** Swindon **Design:** Collett
Diagram: Q.13 **Seats:** 23U **Dimensions:** 52'0" x 8'11"

Seven built.

80943 Dean Forest Railway
80969 Severn Valley Railway
80970 DW80970 National Railway Museum Stored at MoD BAD Kineton
80972 Birmingham Railway Museum
80974 North Yorkshire Moors Railway
80975 DW80975 East Somerset Railway
80976 TDW80976 Rowden Mill Station, Herefordshire

2.2. PASSENGER FULL BRAKES & POST OFFICE VEHICLES

Note: All vehicles in this section are bogied.

PASSENGER BRAKE, GANGWAYED BG

Lot: 1667 **Built:** 1941 **Builder:** Swindon **Design:** Collett
Diagram: K.44 **Dimensions:** 59'10'' x 8'11'' **Type:** Standard

64 Buckinghamshire Railway Centre

Lot: 1665 **Built:** 1945 **Builder:** Swindon **Design:** Collett
Diagram: K.42 **Dimensions:** 57'0''x 8'11'' **Type:** Standard

98 Severn Valley Railway
276 ADB975640 South Devon Railway

Lot: 1512 **Built:** 1934 **Builder:** Swindon **Design:** Collett
Diagram: K.41 **Dimensions:** 57'0'' x 9'0'' **Type:** Standard

111 060790 Didcot Railway Centre

Lot: 1535 **Built:** 1935 **Builder:** Swindon **Design:** Collett
Diagram: K.41 **Dimensions:** 57'0'' x 9'0'' **Type:** Standard

184 ADB975157 Cholsey & Wallingford Railway
185 ADB975158 Gloucestershire-Warwickshire Railway

Lot: 1281 **Built:** 1922 **Builder:** Swindon **Design:** Churchward
Diagram: K.22 **Dimensions:** 56'11'' x 8'11¼'' **Type:** Toplight

261 Pontypool & Blaenavon Railway

Lot: 1722 **Built:** 1949 **Builder:** Swindon **Design:** Hawksworth
Diagram: K.45 **Dimensions:** 64'0'' x 8'11'' **Type:** Standard

295 Steamtown Railway Centre, Carnforth
297 ZDW150354 Northampton & Lamport Railway

Lot: 1740 **Built:** 1950 **Builder:** Swindon **Design:** Hawksworth
Diagram: K.45 **Dimensions:** 64'0'' x 8'11'' **Type:** Standard

316 Nene Valley Railway

Lot: 1752 **Built:** 1951 **Builder:** Swindon **Design:** Hawksworth
Diagram: K.46 **Dimensions:** 64'0'' x 8'11'' **Type:** Standard

329 ADB975795 024529 Carriage & Traction Company Ltd Stored at Crewe Carriage Shed
333 Gloucestershire-Warwickshire Railway
334 Ilderton Station House Cafe & Restaurant

POST OFFICE SORTING VAN POS

Lot: 1430 **Built:** 1929 **Builder:** Swindon **Design:** Collett
Diagram: L.18 **Dimensions:** 57'0'' x 8'6'' **Type:** Bow ended

807 Wessex Traincare Ltd. Body only remains.

POST OFFICE STOWAGE VAN POT

Lot: 1503 **Built:** 1933 **Builder:** Swindon **Design:** Collett
Diagram: L.23 **Dimensions:** 50'0'' x 8'6'' **Type:** Bow ended

812 Wessex Traincare Ltd. Body only remains.

Lot: 1666 **Built:** 1940 **Builder:** Swindon **Design:** Collett
Diagram: L.23 **Dimensions:** 50'0'' x 8'6'' **Type:** Bow ended
Replacement Coach.

814 ADB975156 Didcot Railway Centre

PASSENGER BRAKE, GANGWAYED BG

Lot: 1301 **Built:** 1922 **Builder:** Swindon **Design:** Churchward
Diagram: K.22 **Dimensions:** 56'11'' x 8'11¼'' **Type:** Toplight

1145	079038	Severn Valley Railway
1150	DW150241	Severn Valley Railway

Lot: 1344 **Built:** 1925 **Builder:** Swindon **Design:** Churchward
Diagram: K.36 **Dimensions:** 57'0'' x 9'0'' **Type:** Toplight

Converted to Medical Examination Coach in January 1945, Freight lot 1481, carriage diagram M.33.

1159	DW150294	Didcot Railway Centre

Lot: 1413 **Built:** 1930 **Builder:** Swindon **Design:** Collett
Diagram: K.40 **Dimensions:** 61'4½'' x 9'0'' **Type:** Bow ended

1184		Didcot Railway Centre

2.3. GWR NPCCS TYPES

2.3.1. CARRIAGE TRUCKS

Note: GUVs are bogied vehicles. CCTs have four wheels

GENERAL UTILITY VAN 'MONSTER' GUV

Lot: 1223 **Diagram:** P.18 **Built:** 1911 – 13 **Builder:** Swindon **Dimensions:** 50'0"x 8'6"

484 Didcot Railway Centre

COVERED CARRIAGE TRUCK 'PYTHON' CCT

Lot: 1238 **Diagram:** P.19 **Built:** 1914 **Builder:** Swindon **Dimensions:** 18'0"x 8'10"

565 ADW150265 Didcot Railway Centre

GENERAL UTILITY VAN 'MONSTER' GUV

Lot: 1265 **Diagram:** P.18 **Built:** 1920 **Builder:** Swindon **Dimensions:** 50'0"x 8'6"

594 Gwili Railway

Lot: 1769 **Diagram:** P.24 **Built:** 1954 **Builder:** Swindon **Dimensions:** 50'0"x 8'10"

600 Bluebell Railway

2.3.2. LIVESTOCK VEHICLES

Note: All vehicles in this section have four wheels.

HORSE BOX HB

Lot: 1461 **Diagram:** N.15 **Built:** 1931 **Builder:** Swindon **Dimensions:** 21'0"x 8'7½"

542 Severn Valley Railway Body only remains at Highley.

Lot: 1577 **Diagram:** N.16 **Built:** 1937 **Builder:** Swindon **Dimensions:** 21'0"x 8'7½"

654 Gwili Railway Body only remains
709 ADW150424 Gloucestershire-Warwickshire Railway

SPECIAL CATTLE VAN SCV

Lot: 1774 **Diagram:** W.17 **Built:** 1952 **Builder:** Swindon **Dimensions:**

752 DW150420 Didcot Railway Centre

Lot: **Diagram:** W. ? **Built:** 1953 **Builder:** Swindon **Dimensions:**

765 East Anglian Railway Museum

2.3.3. PERISHABLES VEHICLES

Note: Siphon Gs are bogied vehicles. Milk tanks and Milk Trailer Trucks have six wheels. All other vehicles in this section have four wheels unless stated otherwise.

GANGWAYED MILK VAN SIPHON G

Lot: 1751 **Diagram:** O.62 **Built:** 1951 **Builder:** Swindon **Dimensions:** 50'0"x 8'9½"

1009 Northampton & Lamport Railway
1019 Swindon L. C. & W. Works Ltd
1025 ADB975832 Nottingham Heritage Centre, Ruddington

Lot: 1768 **Diagram:** O.62 **Built:** 1955 **Builder:** Swindon **Dimensions:** 50'0"x 8'9½"

1037 Buckinghamshire Railway Centre
1043 CDB975834 Cholsey & Wallingford Railway

1046 West Somerset Railway
1047 Swindon & Cricklade Railway

Lot: 1396 **Diagram:** O.22 **Built:** 1928 – 29 **Builder:** Swindon **Dimensions:** 50'0''x 8'9½''

1199 ADW150322 Swindon & Cricklade Railway

Lot: 1378 **Diagram:** O.11 **Built:** 1926 – 27 **Builder:** Swindon **Dimensions:** 50'0''x 8'9½''

1257 079060 Severn Valley Railway

Lot: 1721 **Diagram:** O.62 **Built:** 1947 – 50 **Builder:** Swindon **Dimensions:** 50'0''x 8'9½''

1316 Bodmin Steam Railway

MILK BRAKE VAN BM

Lot: 1299 **Diagram:** O.13 **Built:** 1921 **Builder:** Swindon **Dimensions:** 30'0''x 8'11½''

Rebuild of Pharmacy Car 39035.

1399 079062 Severn Valley Railway

MILK TANK MILK

Lot: 1387 **Diagram:** O.44 **Built:** 1927 **Builder:** Swindon **Dimensions:** ' ''x ' ''

Rebuilt from 4-wheel in 1936.

2009 ADW2009 041988 Mangapp's Farm Railway Museum

FISH VAN 'BLOATER' FISH

Lot: 1259 **Diagram:** S.9 **Built:** 1919 **Builder:** Swindon **Dimensions:** 28'10''x 8'7½''

2115 DW150111 Buckinghamshire Railway Centre
2135 DW150295 Gwili Railway Numbered 2745

Lot: 1271 **Diagram:** S.9 **Built:** 1921 **Builder:** Swindon **Dimensions:** 28'10''x 8'7½''

2240 DW150210 Swindon & Cricklade Railway

FRUIT VAN FRUIT A

Lot: 230 **Diagram:** Y.2 **Built:** 1898 **Builder:** Swindon **Dimensions:** ' ''x ' ''

Built as 47833 Under Wagon Lot 230.

2303 DW150063 Severn Valley Railway

FRUIT VAN FRUIT D

Lot: 1765 **Diagram:** Y.14 **Built:** 1952 **Builder:** Swindon **Dimensions:** ' ''x ' ''

2336 024239 Chasewater Railway
2342 Birmingham Railway Museum

FRUIT VAN FRUIT B

Lot: 638 **Diagram:** Y.2 **Built:** 1892 **Builder:** Swindon **Dimensions:** ' ''x ' ''

2356 DW150035 Didcot Railway Centre Built as 47886

FRUIT VAN FRUIT D

Lot: 1765 **Diagram:** Y.14 **Built:** 1952 **Builder:** Swindon **Dimensions:** ' ''x ' ''

2391 TDB975345 060972 Swindon & Cricklade Railway

FRUIT VAN FRUIT C

Lot: 668 **Diagram:** Y.3 **Built:** 1912 **Builder:** Swindon **Dimensions:** 22'0''x 7'10''

2424 KDB975291 Severn Valley Railway Built as 79969

Lot: 667 **Diagram:** Y.3 **Built:** 1912 **Builder:** Swindon **Dimensions:** 22'0''x 7'10''

2487 DW150151 061032 Great Western Museum, Coleford Built as 85987

MILK TANK — MILK

Lot: **Diagram:** O. ? **Built:** 19XX **Builder:** Swindon **Dimensions:** ' ''x ' ''

2506 041358 Carriage & Traction Company Ltd Stored at Ferme Park CS

Lot: 1517 **Diagram:** O.39 **Built:** 1934 **Builder:** Swindon **Dimensions:** ' ''x ' ''

2536 Buckinghamshire Railway Centre

FISH VAN 'BLOATER' — FISH

Lot: 1307 **Diagram:** S.9 **Built:** 1923 **Builder:** Swindon **Dimensions:** 28'0''x 8'7''

2617 DW150267 Tintern Parva Station Museum
2625 DW150236 Llangollen Railway

Lot: 1356 **Diagram:** S.10 **Built:** 1925 **Builder:** Swindon **Dimensions:** 28'0''x 8'7''

2660 DW150169 Llangollen Railway
2661 DW150289 Swanage Railway
2671 DW150160 Didcot Railway Centre

Lot: 1381 **Diagram:** S.11 **Built:** 1928 **Builder:** Swindon **Dimensions:** ' ''x ' ''

2740 DW150352 Tanfield Railway Body only remains. u/f used for GNR ?

GANGWAYED MILK VAN — SIPHON G

Lot: 1578 **Diagram:** O.33 **Built:** 1936 – 37 **Builder:** Swindon **Dimensions:** 50'0''x 8'8¾''

2775 4509 TDW150028 National Railway Museum Rebuilt Post War to Diag M.34
2790 3303 TDW150027 Dean Forest Railway Rebuilt Post War to Diag M.34
2796 Didcot Railway Centre Rebuilt Post War to Diag O.59

FRUIT VAN — FRUIT C

Lot: 1606 **Diagram:** Y.9 **Built:** 1937 **Builder:** Swindon **Dimensions:** ' ''x ' ''

2815 DW150343 070843 Rowden Mill Station, Herefordshire
2823 DW150346 West Somerset Railway
2826 DW150312 Dean Forest Railway Numbered 5521

Lot: 1634 **Diagram:** Y.9 **Built:** 1938 **Builder:** Swindon **Dimensions:** ' ''x ' ''

2851 ADW150309 Swindon & Cricklade Railway
2862 ADW150356 ~~Avon Valley Railway~~ Didcot.

FRUIT VAN — FRUIT D

Lot: 1649 **Diagram:** Y.11 **Built:** 1939 **Builder:** Swindon **Dimensions:** ' ''x ' ''

2876 DW150357 070844 Gloucestershire-Warwickshire Railway
2887 DW150351 Swansea Vale Railway
2902 ADW150318 Dean Forest Railway
2910 ADW150319 West Somerset Railway
2913 DW150363 Swanage Railway

GANGWAYED MILK VAN — SIPHON G

Lot: 1651 **Diagram:** O.33 **Built:** 1938 – 40 **Builder:** Swindon **Dimensions:** 50'0''x 8'8¾''

2926 US 7029 Severn Valley Railway Rebuilt Post War to Diag O.59

Lot: 1664 **Diagram:** O.33 **Built:** 1940 – 45 **Builder:** Swindon **Dimensions:** 50'0''x 8'8¾''

2943 CDB975841 Brighton Railway Museum

Lot: 1664 **Diagram:** O.33 **Built:** 1940 – 45 **Builder:** Swindon **Dimensions:** 50'0''x 8'8¾''

2980 West Somerset Railway
2983 ADB975783 Gloucestershire-Warwickshire Railway
2988 ADB975789 Dean Forest Railway
2994 ADB975843 061057 Bodmin Steam Railway Numbered 1498

MILK TANK — MILK

Lot: ? **Diagram:** O. **Built:** 19xx **Builder:** Swindon **Dimensions:** ' ''x ' ''

3018 ADW3018 041356 West Somerset Railway

MILK TRAILER TRUCK — MILK FLAT

Lot: 1715 **Diagram:** O.58 **Built:** 1947 **Builder:** Swindon **Dimensions:** ' ''x ' ''

3030 Didcot Railway Centre

MILK TANK — MILK

Lot: 1716 **Diagram:** O.57 **Built:** 1946 **Builder:** Swindon **Dimensions:** ' ''x ' ''

3035 ADW3035 East Somerset Railway
3037 ADW3037 South Devon Railway
3043 Gloucestershire-Warwickshire Railway
3052 DW3052 Steamtown Railway Centre, Carnforth

Lot: 1759 **Diagram:** O.64 **Built:** 1950 **Builder:** Swindon **Dimensions:** ' ''x ' ''

3176 Rutland Railway Museum Tank removed

Lot: 1760 **Diagram:** O.56 **Built:** 1952 **Builder:** Swindon **Dimensions:** ' ''x ' ''

3192 ADB975449 041888 North Yorkshire Moors Railway

FRUIT VAN — FRUIT D

Lot: 1723 **Diagram:** Y.14 **Built:** 1950 **Builder:** Swindon **Dimensions:** ' ''x ' ''

3403 TDB975211 Caerphilly Railway
3411 Dean Forest Railway
3412 Llangollen Railway Body only remains
3429 Severn Valley Railway
3436 TDB975300 068724 Cholsey & Wallingford Railway

Lot: 1771 **Diagram:** Y.14 **Built:** 1955 **Builder:** Swindon **Dimensions:** ' ''x ' ''

3448 DB975556 041486 Carriage & Traction Company Ltd Stored at Ferme Park CS
3450 TDB975212 West Somerset Railway

Lot: 1780 **Diagram:** Y.14 **Built:** 1955 **Builder:** Swindon **Dimensions:** ' ''x ' ''

3461 TDB975177 Llangollen Railway
3462 ADB975265 Swindon & Cricklade Railway
3465 DB975411 Llangollen Railway
3467 Severn Valley Railway

MILK TANK — MILK

Lot: **Diagram:** O. ? **Built:** 19XX **Builder:** Swindon **Dimensions:** ' ''x ' ''

???? 079073 Sail & Steam Engineering Ltd

2.3.4. FREIGHT STOCK OFTEN CONFUSED WITH PERISHABLES VEHICLES

SIX-WHEELED WATER TANK — WATER TANK

Lot: 1555 **Diagram:** DD.6 **Built:** 1946 **Builder:** Swindon **Dimensions:** ' ''x ' ''

101 DW101W Didcot Railway Centre

102	ADW 102	West Somerset Railway	
106	ADW 106	Titley Junction Station, near Kington	

GOODS VAN MINK D

Lot: 510 **Diagram:** V.9 **Built:** 1906 **Builder:** Swindon **Dimensions:** ' ''x ' ''

28709	DW28709	Pontypool & Blaenavon Railway	
28804	DW28804	Caerphilly Railway	

Lot: 660 **Diagram:** V.11 **Built:** 1911 **Builder:** Swindon **Dimensions:** ' ''x ' ''

28833	ADW204	Llangollen Railway	
28899		Tanfield Railway	Rebuilt as 'BALCONY SALOON No.1'
288XX		Oswestry Cycle & Railway Museum	Body only remains
28918		Caerphilly Railway	

GOODS VAN MINK G

Lot: 1067 **Diagram:** V.22 **Built:** 1930–31 **Builder:** Swindon **Dimensions:** ' ''x ' ''

112835	042432	North Yorkshire Moors Railway	
112843		Didcot Railway Centre	
112857	070848	Dean Forest Railway	
112884	042431	National Railway Museum	
112889		Severn Valley Railway	
1128XX		Gloucestershire-Warwickshire Railway	Body only remains at Toddington Yard

3. SOUTHERN RAILWAY STOCK

3.0. INTRODUCTION

It may come as a surprise to many readers that preserved Southern Railway (SR) Non-Passenger Carrying Coaching Stock outnumbers Passenger Carrying Coaching Stock by more than four to one! The longevity of the predominantly wooden bodied Southern Railway designs of the former resulted in the majority surviving well into the 1970s, indeed the final withdrawals from capital stock did not take place until 1986 with many surviving beyond then in departmental service. The Southern Railway, unlike its contemporaries, adopted separate numbering schemes for passenger carrying and non-passenger carrying coaching stock, thus various duplicate numbers occurred. Numbering was however to a general pattern which grouped vehicles of similar design together although filling of vacate number ranges did occur particularly in respect of non-passenger carrying coaching stock.

Coaching stock covered in this section is considered in three categories. Firstly the Ironclad stock of the London & South Western Railway which continued in production in early Southern Railway days. Secondly, Southern Railway design passenger carrying coaching stock and Thirdly Southern Railway design non-passenger carrying coaching stock.

Separate number series existed on the Southern Railway for passenger carrying and non-passenger carrying coaching stock thus it is possible to have duplicate numbers and indeed this occurs in preservation with 1464 from both series being preserved.

Similar to Pullman Car Company stock the author considers that in certain respects the definitive book covering the 'nuts and bolts' of Southern Railway coaching stock remains to be written. However a trio of books written by David Gould are particularly recommended which contain the majority of 'nuts & bolts' information likely to be required in addition to giving a good insight into the vehicles covered here, these being:-

Maunsell's S.R. steam passenger stock 1923-1939/David Gould.-Salisbury:The Oakwood Press,1978.

Bullied's S.R. steam passenger stock/David Gould.-Salisbury:The Oakwood Press,1980.

Southern Railway Passenger Vans/David Gould.-Salisbury:The Oakwood Press,1992.

3.0.1. LOADING GAUGE

As has already been referred to in the Pullman section the Southern Railway line between Tonbridge and Battle was once of a restrictive loading gauge often referred to as "Hastings Gauge". This had been the result of shoddy nineteenth century workmanship with the tunnels on the route being clad with insufficient layers of brickwork. Thus extra layers of brickwork were subsequently added consequently restricting the width and height of the tunnels. Thus only carriages of restricted dimensions were able to pass along the route. The situation was complicated still further as the section of line between Tonbridge and Grove Junction (Tunbridge Wells) through Somerhill Tunnel was less restrictive than that between Grove Junction and Battle. In order to ensure only carriages of exceptable dimensions operated along the route a system of 'restrictions' was established with all vehicles being given a restriction as follows:-

RESTRICTION 0 May pass over all routes of the Southern Railway.

RESTRICTION 1 May pass over all routes except between Grove Junction and Battle.

RESTRICTION 4 May pass over all routes except between Tonbridge and Battle.

Details of the restriction of vehicles in this section are given in the headings for individual orders of vehicles.

Generally it was carriages intended for use on services via Tunbridge Wells to Hastings which were constructed to restriction 'O' and carriages intended for use on services via Tunbridge Wells and Eridge between London and the South Coast which were constructed to restriction '1'.

It was not until the 1980s when the Tonbridge East Junction-Bo-Peep Junction section was electrified that the restrictive problems were overcome by reducing the tunnels to reversible single track operation. British Rail itself having gone to the expense of constructing diesel electric locomotives and multiple units of restricted dimensions for use on services via this route.

First class compartments contained six seats in restriction 0 vehicles, but only four seats in restriction 1 and 4 vehicles. Third class compartments contained eight seats in restriction 0 and 1 vehicles, but only six seats in restriction 4 vehicles. Thus in restriction 1 vehicles, first class passengers had twice the width as third class passengers!

3.0.2. IRONCLAD STOCK

At the time of the grouping in 1923 construction was underway by the London and South Western Railway of the distinctive Ironclad stock, production continuing into Southern Railways days. Details of all the preserved Ironclad stock is included here, both London & South Western Railway and Southern Railway built. It will be noted that all that surviving has seen departmental service which has resulted in the interiors of many being far from complete.

The first 'Ironclad' stock was constructed by the London & South Western Railway in 1921 for the Bournemouth line. It consisted of four five coach pantry sets formed Corridor Brake Third, Pantry Third, Corridor First, Corridor Third, Corridor Brake Third. These sets had the distinctive 'Ironclad' appearance being steel clad with 57' 0'' body length. Two carriages survive from these sets, Corridor Third 717 at the former Horsebridge station and Corridor Brake Third 3187 at Mangapps Farm Railway museum. Both were extensively gutted when in departmental service and now see use as museum coaches.

Six five coach sets were completed in 1923, these were similarly formed to the 1921 sets however the Pantry Third was replaced with a further Corridor Third. In addition two Dining Saloons were constructed in order to augment the sets as required whilst older wooden-panelled dining saloons were also used when needed. One of the Dining Cars, 7851, survives on the Watercress Line along with Corridor Brake Third 3190 awaiting restoration whilst Corridor Third 730 is similarly located on the Kent & East Sussex Railway. A further two from these sets are also listed below, Corridor Third 728 and Corridor Brake Third 3193. These were earmarked, along with several other unrestored carriages, as part of a scheme to recreate a set of 'Ironclad' stock for use on preserved lines. Little has been heard of this project recently and regrettably it now appears that this scheme may have foundered. A recent development however has been the movement of Corridor Third 728 to the former station at West Bay, Dorset along with BR Mark I TSO 4074. Both are currently in use as part of the Visitor Information Centre being established at this location.

In 1924 a number of 'loose' Corridor Thirds, Corridor Firsts and Corridor Composites were constructed. Two of the Corridor Thirds and one of the Corridor Firsts survive although all are awaiting restoration. Corridor Third 748 and Corridor First 7200 are located at the Kent & East Sussex Railway were it is understood they were to be restored as part of the above mentioned scheme. The other Corridor Third 752 is unlikely ever to be restored. This has had the body removed for use as a storage shed by the Isle of Wight Steam Railway, the intention being that a much older body will be placed on the underframe at a future date.

The only other 'Ironclad' preserved is Corridor Brake Third 3204. This was constructed in 1925 as part of a five coach set for Waterloo-Bournemouth workings. For many years it has been located at the West Somerset Railway awaiting restoration by its owners the Somerset & Dorset Railway Trust.

All the preserved 'Ironclads' have seen departmental service prior to preservation, a factor which obviously led to their survival. Of particular interest are Corridor Thirds 717, 730, 748 and Corridor First 7200 which were amongst eight 'Ironclads' numbered DS225-232 and converted to Breakdown Train Coaches in 1958. These survived in use until the mid-1980s before being replaced with more modern vehicles. The final allocations being ADS225 & ADS226 at Bournemouth, ADS227, ADS228 & ADS231 at Wimbledon, ADS229 & ADS230 at Hither Green and ADS232 at Brighton. Of those not preserved ADS225 converted from Corridor Third 724, ADS231 converted from Brake Corridor Third 3182 and ADS232 converted from Brake Corridor Third 3198 have been scrapped whilst ADS230 converted from Corridor Third 753 continues in departmental service. In 1960 a further eight 'Ironclads' were converted to Breakdown Train Coaches numbered DS70010-70017. Only two of these Corridor Thirds 728 and 752 have survived in preservation, however Corridor Brake Third 3190 latterly TDW70016 was also preserved for many years at the Watercress Line but has now been broken up. The remains of one other do however survive, this being Corridor Third 760, latterly TDW70013, the body of which is used as stables at Harthill, South Yorkshire (SK 494800).

It can be concluded that preservation has not been kind to the 'Ironclad' stock with no carriages having yet been fully restored. Fortunately the majority of types survive in sufficient number to create realistic sets. It is hoped the aims of the a aforementioned preservation proposal to create such a set will one day be fulfilled.

The layout of details of the preserved 'Ironclad' coaches generally conforms to information given in 'Guide to Layout' however several carriages were initially numbered in the London & South Western Railway numbering series. Thus the first number column gives the LSWR. number were applicable followed by the Southern Railway number.

3.0.3. SR PASSENGER-CARRYING COACHING STOCK

Forty eight carriages are listed in this section of which two exist as nothing more than underframes. This being the smallest preserved representation of any of the grouping companies. Carriages are listed numerically by their Southern Railway numbers, the majority of which only ever carried one capital stock number. A peculiarity of the Southern Railway was that their order number could apply to carriages of various designs. This being due to normally ordering by complete sets rather than by fleets of vehicles.

The carriages conveniently fit into two main eras of construction. Firstly their are those to the designs of Maunsell which were built before the Second World War. Secondly there are those to the designs of Bulleid which were built after the Second World War.

3.0.3.1. Maunsell Stock

The first phase of Maunsell designs was authorised in 1925. Each coach had a body length of 59' and width of 9'. The body had rounded sides and bowed ends, the frame was largely of wood, with steel sheeting; roofs were wood, canvas-covered. The compartment side of the coach had a door leading into every compartment, but on the corridor side there was generally a door opposite each alternate compartment.

The oldest of the preserved carriages dates from 1927, this being Third Class Dining Car 7866. It was constructed as part of an order for six Third Class Dining Cars to work on the western section were it ran paired with a First Class Kitchen Dining Car. At that time it seated 64 people in three saloons with fixed, tip up seating. It was reclassified and renumbered as an Open Third in 1930 taking the number 1365, the number it is listed as in the following. At the time it was decided to stop providing special vehicles for catering. In 1944 the coach was requisitioned as an ambulance coach and numbered 6802 as part of Ambulance Train 68. It returned to traffic in 1947 as a Third Class Dining Saloon numbered 7841 following a reversal of previous policy. In 1949 it was rebuilt with two saloons as a composite dining coach seating 30 third class and 24 first class passengers on loose seats. Having seen considerable use on the Bluebell Railway following preservation this carriage currently awaits further restoration.

In 1926 an order was placed for two eight coach sets for use on Kent Coast and Eastbourne services which were delivered in 1928. One carriage from these sets has survived in preservation this being Corridor Composite 5153 which was built to Restriction '1' dimensions. This carriage saw a number of years service on the Kent & East Sussex Railway were it is now stored awaiting full restoration.

In 1928 a slight change in design was made to the coaches with modifications made in order to incorporate higher windows in the corridors. However the windows at each end of the coaches remained at the original height in order to allow the placing of destination board brackets above the windows.

Well known to many and still running today are the through workings from Bournemouth to North East England. In 1929 new stock was provided for these services and one of the carriages, Corridor Brake Composite 6575, has survived. This was initially intended for use on the Bradford portion of the Bournemouth-Newcastle working but it is believed that it was soon to be found elsewhere on the workings. Latterly it was to be found on West of England main line where it again was utilised for portion working. This carriage has been meticulously restored by the Bluebell Railway were it now sees regular use.

Also dating from 1929 is Corridor First 7400 which was constructed for use on the restricted loading gauge Tonbridge-Battle route to Restriction 'O'. It being used in trains running between London, Bexhill and Hastings. Following withdrawal in 1961 this coach became a S&T department work study coach. It currently awaits restoration on the Kent & East Sussex Railway. It being one of only a few of the distinctive Restriction 'O' carriages that survive.

In April 1929 an order was placed for twenty Open Thirds, fifty Corridor Brake Composites, twenty Nondescript Saloons and ten First Class Kitchen and Dining Cars. Examples of all but the later were preserved. The Open Third was an entirely new type. It had recessed end doors for passenger access, two saloon compartments, one of four seating bays and one of three, with two and two seating and a central gangway. At each end of the vehicle was an entrance vestibule and a lavatory compartment. It was intended that the coaches should be employed largely as trailers to Kitchen & Dining Cars. Open Third 1381 saw use as a Staff and Tool Coach with the Power Supply Section following withdrawal. It is now located at the Swanage Railway were in recent years it has had considerable attention resulting in it now being occasionally used for passenger services. Nondescript Saloon 7798 at the Kent & East Sussex Railway awaits its turn for restoration. Corridor Brake Composite 6601 was preserved at the Watercress Line but in recent years, firstly the body was removed with parts being taken for other carriages and more recently the underframe has been broken up.

This was followed by a further large order in June 1929 for two hundred carriages. Preserved vehicles being 3724 a Corridor Brake Third intended for Waterloo, Bournemouth, Swanage and Weymouth services. 3719 a Corridor Brake Third intended for Waterloo-Portsmouth services. 5644 a Corridor Composite intended for London, Worthing and Littlehampton services. 2356 a Corridor Third intended for London-Eastbourne services, this being built to Restriction '1' to allow its use on services routed via Tunbridge Wells. 5618 a Corridor Composite for London, Eastbourne and Hastings services again constructed to Restriction '1'. Corridor Brake Thirds 3687 & 3690 and Corridor Composite 5600 intended for London, Bexhill and Hastings services built to Restriction 'O' for use on the Tonbridge-Battle route. 5618 is the only one not to have seen some other use between withdrawal and preservation. Following withdrawal, along with 5153 above, it was preserved on the Kent & East Sussex Railway were following many years occasional use it is now stored pending full overhaul. 3724 and 5644 saw further use with Chipmans as Weedkilling train coaches normally working together in the same train. Current plans for this pair, now preserved on the Bluebell Railway is for them to be restored in this guise. Restriction 'O' Corridor Brake Thirds 3687 & 3690 owe their survival to being included for many years in the once secret emergency control trains which were kept for use during periods of national crisis, fortunately never being used for this. Their good condition ensured further departmental use following the disbanding of these trains. Both now await restoration. The third Restriction 'O' coach, Corridor Composite 5600 was a familiar sight on the Southern Region for many years were it was used as an Instruction Coach. It now awaits restoration at the Rother Valley Railway. 2356 had its original interior stripped out when converted for use as an office coach at Streatham Common, it now sees use as a volunteer staff coach at the Bluebell Railway with no plans as yet to restore its interior.

Corridor Brake Third 2768 was constructed in 1932 as part of an order for twenty four coach sets for use on London, Portsmouth, Bournemouth and West of England services. This carriage being initially used on West of England services. This coach has been restored at the Swanage Railway following a period in departmental use as a Power Supply Section Staff & Tool Coach. These were the first carriages to incorporate the modified lavatory ventilator. This comprised two narrow bonnets, one above the other, instead of the single one that had hitherto been provided.

The only preserved Southern Railway First Class Kitchen & Dining Car dates from 1932. This being 7864 which was one of ten built that year. When built it had seating for 24 first class diners. In 1947, in a rethink on catering provision, this was cut to 8 seats, the rest being replaced by a buffet counter. Following preservation by the Bluebell Railway it served for twenty years as a static refreshment room, it now however awaits extensive restoration.

A further large order was placed in 1932 for 210 carriages, these consisted 100 Corridor Thirds, 50 Open Thirds, 30 Corridor Brake Thirds, 20 Nondescript Brakes and 10 First Class Kitchen and Dining Cars. Those preserved being Open Thirds 1323, 1336 and 1346, Nondescript Open Brakes 4432, 4438, 4441, 4443 and 4444 and Corridor Third 1020 built to Restriction 'O' for use on the Tonbridge-Battle route.

Following withdrawal in 1964 Open Third 1323 saw a number of years use as an Instruction Coach at various locations on the Southern Region of British Railways. It now awaits restoration at the Watercress Line were it has been stored for many years since arriving from Basingstoke in 1982. 1336 and 1346 had similar histories following withdrawal in 1961, both seeing many years use as Office Coaches before passing into the hands of preservationists. 1336 moving to the Bluebell Railway and 1346 to the Kent & East Sussex Railway. 1346 retains all its internal partitions and lavatories as well as some original seating making it particularly suited to early restoration.

The Nondescript Brakes were intended mainly for Continental Boat Trains, they were most interesting and unusual vehicles. There were six seating bays with 36 seats, all having individual arms. Reading from the brake end, the first, fourth and sixth bay had a door leading into the space between the seats; the second, third and fifth bays had a large fixed window with small sliding windows above it, one lavatory was provided. In 1959 four of them including 4438 & 4444 were converted into Ambulance Ward Cars, Nos. 7920 to 7923. Each car had 11 seats and 24 cots. Two of these, 7920 and 7923 were the last Southern Railway passenger carrying coaches in normal service, being withdrawn in 1971. Following a period of storage 7920 became DB975279 in 1973 and was placed at the seaward end of Dover Marine pier as a Staff & Tool Coach, passing for preservation in 1980 to the Kent & East Sussex Railway where it awaits restoration. 7923 became Tunnel Gauging Coach DB975406 in 1974 passing to the Watercress Line for preservation in 1978, regrettably however it was broken up there in 1987.

Corridor Third 1020 represents the final build of locomotive hauled coaching stock for use on through London-Tonbridge-Hastings workings. It being the late 1950s before further stock was constructed, this being the distinctive build of Diesel units many of which have now been preserved. 1020 was withdrawn in 1959 following the introduction of these units. It passed into departmental service as a Civil Engineers Staff and Tool Coach which resulted in the almost complete removal of the carriages original interior. The carriage awaits restoration at the Kent & East Sussex Railway and is considered a very long term project.

We now come to what is known as later Maunsell Corridor Stock. These had different body styling to earlier carriages. The windows were virtually flush with the body-sides, which exhibited large quantities of screw heads. The earliest order of these was for 30 Open Thirds and one of these 1309 has been preserved on the Bluebell Railway. This has seven seating bays, each with a large window equipped with two sliding ventilator glasses. The top quarters of these windows were square-cornered, but the lower quarters had large-radius rounded corners. Lavatory windows each had two ventilator bonnets above them. Entry to the coach was by end doors, which were slightly re-cessed. Although much of the interior of 1309 was destroyed when it was used in departmental service as a mobile office a most thorough restoration has taken place and this carriage can be savoured by passengers on the Bluebell Railway.

Further examples of this flush sided stock were built in 1935 and three Corridor Brake Composites survive. 6686 spent its service life on the South Eastern section, gaining in 1960, along with 6685, electric heating to allow it to run on the 'Night Ferry' service. These were withdrawn from service in 1966 and had the distinction of being the last survivors, not rebuilt, of the Southern Railways pre-war passenger carrying coaching stock on British Rail. 6686 has seen many years service on the Bluebell before being recently taken out of service for a thorough overhaul. 6697 and 6699 were formed as part of two coach sets which ran Waterloo-Swanage - Lymington and Waterloo-West of England services. In 1959-1960 they were amongst twenty Corridor Brake Composites chosen for inclusion in two coach Push Pull Sets to be matched with Open Thirds, 1323 above being one of the Open Thirds. Following withdrawal these became spray coaches for use on Chipman operated weedkilling trains which resulted in much of the original interiors being removed.

Further Maunsell design carriages were constructed in 1936 but none of these survive.

3.0.3.2. Bulleid Stock

After this a gap of ten years in locomotive hauled passenger carriage construction occurred. It not being until after the second world war that further carriages were constructed, these being to the designs of Bulleid. The first of these appeared in 1945-46 but no examples have been preserved.

In 1947 twenty four three coach sets were constructed consisting of a Corridor Composite sandwiched between Semi-open Brake Thirds. Two of the Corridor Composites survive both coming straight from service into preservation and both 5761 on the Swanage Railway and 5768 on the Bluebell Railway can be savoured by passengers.

During 1947-1948 eleven six coach sets were constructed for Bournemouth Line workings. Several carriages surviving from these. Open Thirds 1456 and 1457 and Semi-open Brake Thirds 4365, 4366 and 4367. The Open Thirds were fitted with tables, had a transverse vestibule at one end, a four bay saloon with 32 seats, a centre vestibule, another 32 seat saloon, a transverse vestibule and two lavatories adjoining a centre corridor at the other end of the coach. 1456 which is part of the National Collection saw use as an Office Coach following withdrawal, it is currently on loan to the Bluebell Railway. 1457 saw departmental service as a Civil Engineers Tunnel Inspection Coach and now awaits restoration at the Swanage Railway. The Semi-open Brake Thirds had a guard's and luggage compartment, with a set of double doors each side and outward opening door for the guard. Next came two compartments, with side corridor on the left-hand side as one looked away from the luggage compartment. Then came a lavatory, rather unusually in the middle of the coach. A transverse vestibule, with external doors, was located between the lavatory and a four bay open saloon, with two and two facing seats and a central walkway. Finally a further transverse vestibule with external doors at the inner end of the coach. All three saw military service following withdrawal which resulted in them surviving almost complete excluding the effects of old age. 4365 has been the beneficiary of considerable attention at Swanage and is now available for occasional passenger use. 4366 and 4367 are both stored awaiting restoration, a task which should not be as great as that needed for many other preserved Southern Railway carriages.

During the late 1940s several carriages were constructed by the Birmingham Railway Carriage and Wagon Company. Three of these, all Semi-open Brake Thirds have been preserved following periods of departmental use. Of the two at the Bluebell Railway 4279 has been fully restored whilst 4227 requires attention as does 4211 on the Watercress Line.

1949 saw the introduction of 15 four coach sets formed Semi-open Brake Third, Corridor Third, Corridor Composite, Semi-open Brake Third. Two of the Semi-open Brake Thirds have been preserved following periods of use as Staff & Dormitory coaches in Chipmans weedkilling trains. 4035 has remained stored at the North Yorkshire Moors Railway since its purchase whilst 4036 at the Bluebell Railway has been reduced to its underframe.

In 1950 twelve five coach sets entered service formed Semi-open Brake Third, Corridor Third, Corridor Composite, Corridor Third, Semi-open Brake Third. A recent entry into preservation is Semi-open

Brake Third 4008 from one of these sets. Latterly this has been in departmental service being used as an instruction coach. It is currently located at the Bluebell Railway although a movement by its owners the Venice-Simplon Orient Express to their Stewarts Lane depot is likely in the not too distant future.

During 1950-51 a further forty five loose Open Thirds were constructed, not surprisingly many of these survived into the preservation era with three being purchased almost straight from service whilst the one that did see departmental use was little altered. 1464, 1481 and 1482 see regular use on the Bluebell Railway. 1469, one of the few preserved Southern carriages not to be preserved in Southern Railway territory, is normally available for examination at Ingrow on the Kieghley and Worth Valley Railway.

The last Bulleid stock to be constructed was for 16 sets of Semi-open Brake Third, Corridor Composite, Semi-open Brake Third. Two of the Semi-open Brake Thirds have now been preserved. 2515 is now fully restored on the Bluebell Railway following a long period of storage prior to preservation. A more recent entry to preservation is 2526 which has recently been obtained by the Venice-Simplon Orient Express following many years service on the Southern Region as an Instruction Coach following withdrawal from capital stock.

3.0.4. SR NON-PASSENGER-CARRYING COACHING STOCK

Probably the most surprising feature of the items of Southern Railway design coaching stock preserved is that the non-passenger carrying types out number the passenger carrying types by four to one. In addition the majority of those preserved are of the same design, namely the 4-wheeled Luggage Van latterly referred to as Parcels and Miscellaneous van. If there is one non-passenger type that typifies the Southern Railway it is this four-wheeled van. The design originated with the South Eastern & Chatham Railway in 1919 when one prototype vehicle was constructed. The design being maintained through until the last British Rail built vans of 1951. For completeness all such vans are included here. Fortunately the prototype passed into departmental service and has been subsequently restored at the Kent & East Sussex Railway before moving to its current home at the Rother Valley Railway. A considerable number of four wheeled vans have been acquired by preservationists as a source of underframes for ancient carriage bodies recovered from farm yards and similar delightful locations. Thus the van bodies themselves becoming grounded bodies or regrettably in some cases broken up.

As with Passenger Carrying Coaching Stock vehicles are again listed in numerical order by their Southern Railway number, this being the only capital stock number carried by the majority of the preserved vehicles. The exception being that the South Eastern & Chatham Railway built vehicles included were renumbered by the Southern Railway, both numbers being shown in chronological order for these. Although a planned numbering scheme was introduced by the Southern Railway at the grouping this was not strictly adhered to with several orders taking up gaps left in the series or numbers of withdrawn vehicles. However, with a few exceptions, vehicles of a particular type tend to be grouped together in this listing. Many of the vehicles listed here saw departmental service after withdrawal and details of numbers carried are given after the Southern Railway number. It should also be noted that vehicles transferred for use on the Isle of Wight were numbered in a special series. Preserved vans included in this series have the Isle of Wight number shown after the Southern Railway number prefixed IOW.

It is probably best to consider the 4-wheeled Luggage Van or Parcels and Miscellaneous Van first as several other designs are derived from this most successful vehicle. The design originated with a prototype passenger luggage van constructed by the South Eastern and Chatham Railway at Ashford works in 1919. This van had a body length of 32' and width of 9'0'' and employed a construction of light steel framework planked internally with wooden boards. The height from rail to top of the roof was 12' and the wheel base was 21'. Its construction owed more to the technique of goods van building than of passenger construction, this however was to be the norm with the vast majority of Southern Railway non passenger carrying coaching stock. Features included two sets of double doors on each body side and four fixed windows protected on the inside by horizontal bars. A lozenge-shaped panel used for chalking destinations was located below the two outer-end windows but not the two centre windows. The roof had an elliptical profile and was made of wooden boards covered with canvas which had four torpedo ventilators mounted on it. In addition an angled steel ventilator cover was fitted top centre in each body end. Internally there were two interconnected luggage compartments of slightly unequal length. This van was numbered 132 by the South Eastern & Chatham Railway being renumbered 1972 by the Southern Railway. Fortunately upon its withdrawal this van was transferred to departmental stock ensuring its survival. It has now been preserved by the Rother Valley Railway and is displayed at Robertsbridge.

The prototype obviously proved satisfactory as the South Eastern & Chatham Railway then ordered twenty from the Bristol Carriage and Wagon Company in 1921, the only difference being that a chalking panel was added under all windows. Regrettably none of these vans have survived, however four from a further batch of twenty four built at Ashford in 1922 do survive in preservation following periods of departmental use.

It was 1933 before the Southern Railway ordered any further vans, however in this year fifty were ordered from Ashford works to be numbered 2181-2230. These very closely resembled the South Eastern & Chatham Railway examples, the principle detail difference being that they had four body side ventilators, each protected by an angled steelhood, below each of the four chalk panels which in turn were immediately below each window. Internally there was no partition resulting in one large open space. Several of this order have been preserved. Orders then followed at fairly regular intervals with the final order being placed in British Railways days for construction at Wolverton works. Vans from this later order were numbered 1451-1500 and examples from this and all the other orders have been preserved.

Very similar in design were the 4-wheel Utility Vans or Covered Carriage Trucks. These are very similar to the 4-wheel luggage vans built by the Southern Railway with the addition of end outward opening double doors and a small drop door so that road vehicles could be driven straight in. The first fifty were constructed by the Midland Railway Carriage & Wagon Company in 1928 and numbered 2023-2072. Regrettably none of these have been preserved. Subsequently Ashford works built a further 140 to four separate orders, examples of all being preserved. A further fifty followed in 1938 with Ashford underframes and Eastleigh bodies, these being numbered 1731-1780, with several examples preserved. The final orders came in British Railways days with one hundred being built at Ashford in 1951 and fifty being built at Lancing in 1955, examples of both orders being preserved.

Non-Gangwayed full brakes come in two distinct types, four-wheeled and bogied. Turning firstly too the four wheelers. These are in fact a stretched version of the standard Parcels and Miscellaneous van described above having a body length of 36'. The first batch of fifty were ordered in 1936 with Ashford built underframes and Eastleigh built bodies, these were numbered 400-449 and several have been preserved. Each van has a central guards compartment with outward opening doors at cross corners flanked by two luggage compartments. A further one hundred were ordered in 1937 and numbered 651-750. The first twenty were built at Ashford whilst the remainder had Ashford underframes and Eastleigh bodies. One example of each has been preserved although the later example has had the body removed from the underframe. A further fifty were constructed in 1939 again with Ashford underframes and Eastleigh bodies, numbered 751-800, a couple of which have been preserved. Finally a further batch of fifty was constructed during the war with Lancing built underframes and Eastleigh bodies, numbered 931-980, the first of these being preserved at the Llangollen railway. Additionally in 1941 five further vans were constructed with safes numbered 10-14. These vans had Lancing built underframes and Eastleigh bodies, fortunately one of these survives on the Swanage railway.

A further stretching occurred to create the bogie version of the full brake which had a 50' body. As with the four wheelers they had a centrally located guards compartment flanked by two large luggage compartments. There were four sets of double doors on each body side but no fixed windows in the body, nor were there end gangways. The first fifty vans were ordered in 1938 and had Ashford underframes and Eastleigh bodies being numbered 350-399. Fortunately one of these has been preserved at the Swanage Railway. A further batch of fifty soon followed numbered 201-250, it being from this batch that the majority of those preserved are drawn. A final batch of thirty numbered 251-280 were constructed at Lancing in British Railways days of which three have now been preserved. Like all the distinctive Southern Railway vans these were constructed to Restriction 'O' which ensured many survived until the completion of the electrification/modernisation of the Tonbridge East Junction-Bo Peep Junction route, these vans being employed on Newspaper trains headed by the distinctive Restriction 'O' Class 33/2 diesel-electric locomotives.

The general utility van referred to by the Southern Railway as a Bogie Luggage Van is in fact a stretched version of the four wheel luggage van with gangways. They had three sets of double doors and six fixed windows each side. The first fifty of these were ordered in 1928. They utilised the underframes from withdrawn London & South Western Railway suburban passenger carriages and had a body length of 51' 3''. The new bodies were fitted at Ashford and the vans numbered 2281-2330, regrettably known of this first order has been preserved. A further order was placed in 1929 for a further forty. The first fourteen had 51' 3'' bodies whilst the remainder had 53' 3'' bodies. One of the shorter examples has been preserved by the Rother Valley Railway and is now located at Robertsbridge. Finally a further thirty were ordered in 1930, the first twenty one with 53' 3'' bodies numbered 2461-2481 and the later nine with 51' 3'' bodies numbered 2482-2490. One of the long ones is preserved at the Bluebell Railway. Also still existing is 2464. This was the van used to convey the coffin of Sir Winston Churchill from Waterloo to Handborough on 30th January 1965. For this duty it was painted in pullman colours. It was subsequently exported to the United States of America, leaving aboard Royal Mail Lines vessel 'Dongedyk' on 28th October 1965. Following extensive enquiries it has recently been confirmed as being located at Industry Hills Sheraton Resort & Conference Centre, One Industry Hills Parkway, City of Industry, near Los Angeles California, where it is used as a store.

Special Cattle Vans, used for conveying prize cattle in relative comfort compared with ordinary open-sided cattle trucks, rather resembled horse boxes in appearance. Where as cattle trucks were classed as goods stock, special cattle vans were definitely passenger-rated stock. Fifty special cattle vans were ordered by the Southern Railway in 1929, construction being undertaken by the Birmingham Carriage and Wagon Company. The majority were withdrawn from service in the early 1960s. However two were extensively rebuilt as train steam-heating boiler vans in 1962. One of this pair has fortunately survived to be preserved at the Bo'ness and Kinneil Railway. The other one, 3703 (ADS70191) was scrapped in 1982, having latterly been used at Oxford. In 1952 a further ten were constructed under British Railways at Lancing, fortunately one of these now forms part of the national collection and is located at the National Railway Museum at York were it is now stored awaiting further restoration following periods on display.

The Southern Railway constructed over sixty milk tanks of which two have been preserved. 4409 is of particular interest as the tank was first carried on a four wheel chassis. Such chassis were quickly found to be unsuitable for milk tanks thus in 1938 a replacement six wheeled chassis was fitted. Surprisingly, considering its pedigree this vehicle is preserved at Didcot Railway Centre. 4430 was built for use by United Dairies in 1933 and now restored is often active on the Bluebell Railway.

Thirty Bogie Scenery Vans or General Utility Vans were constructed in three batches of ten at approximately ten yearly intervals. These vans were around fifty foot in length depending on the particular order but the special feature was the very high arched, steel roof, making the vehicles 12' 8'' from rail to top of the roof. The vans, which also had end-loading doors, were intended for carriage of large items such as theatrical scenery, circus equipment and even elephants for which several had strengthened floors. This feature resulting in all thirty being nicknamed 'elephant vans'. The first ten built at Eastleigh utilised underframes from London, Brighton and South Coast Railway coaches and were numbered 4577-4586, regrettably none of these survive. 1938 saw the construction of a further ten, this time with new Ashford underframes and Eastleigh bodies, numbered 4587-4596. Four of these have been preserved whilst a fifth sees use with Nomix-Chipman as a Leaf Jetting Van, this being one of three with the strengthened floor for conveying elephants. The final batch of ten was built at Lancing works soon after nationalisation and numbered 4597-4606. Three of these are preserved including elephant van proper 4601 at the Bluebell Railway whilst Nomix-Chipman retain a further one as a spare spray van and one is located at Wessex Train Care, Eastleigh. It is anticipated that the pair with Nomix-Chipman will shortly be disposed of following the acquisition of three BR-design GUVs which were modified for Motorail use for conversion to spraying vans.

Eight Post Office Vans were constructed by the Southern Railway, the only non-passenger carrying vehicles built which resembled passenger carrying coaching stock. The first van was completed in 1936 and was a sorting van numbered 4919. It had a body length of 58' and width of 9'. There was one set of double doors on one side and two sliding doors on the other. To conform to standard practise for mail vans at that time, off-centre gangways were fitted at both ends. Regrettably this van has not survived. In 1939 three further sorting vans were built at Eastleigh based on the original with the addition of a lavatory compartment and adjacent sink, these were numbered 4920-4922. To go with the sorting vans four stowage vans were constructed with Lancing underframes and Eastleigh bodies and numbered 4957-4960. They had the same overall dimensions as the sorting vans and, like them, were fitted with off centre gangways. Otherwise they were just empty shells, without sorting pigeon holes, access was by two sliding doors on each body side and illumination was given by small toplights. Two of the sorting vans and one of the stowage vans have been preserved.

For those wishing to read further about these vehicles the book Southern Railway Passenger Vans by David Gould referred to above is strongly recommended.

Finally mention should be made of a couple of outstanding queries which the author has as yet been able to resolve. Firstly mention is made of Parcels & Miscellaneous Van bodies 1119 and 1225. Following removal from their respective underframes these were located at Wittersham Road station on the Kent & East Sussex Railway. During the early 1990s one of these bodies disappeared. Regrettably it has not been able to establish which is the survivor and the destiny of the other, this is not for want of trying. The author has written twice to the Kent & East Sussex Railway on this matter and still awaits a reply, indeed in recent years this particular railway seems to have adopted a rather negative attitude towards those with an interest in its coaching stock! Secondly mention is made of the three Parcels & Miscellaneous Van bodies in preservation for which the numerical identity is not known. Both the Pontypool & Blaenavon Railway and West Somerset Railway have been extremely helpful with regard to establishing the identities but without success. The body at Wessex Traincare has been there for many years. Did anyone record its identity on a visit to the works in past years? Can any readers of this book solve these mysteries?

3.1. LSWR/SR 'IRONCLAD' STOCK

Note: All these coaches are restriction 4. The first column gives the LSWR number.

CORRIDOR THIRD TK

Diagram: 24 **Built**: 1921 **Builder**: Eastleigh **Seats**: 64T **Dimensions**: 57′0′′ x 9′0′′

Built for use in five coach Bournemouth line pantry sets 431 – 434.

773 717 ADS226 Horsebridge Station, Kings Sombre

Diagram: 24 **Built**: 1923 **Builder**: Eastleigh **Seats**: 64T **Dimensions**: 57′0′′ x 9′0′′

Built for use in five coach sets 435 – 440.

74 728 ADS70011 West Bay Visitor Information Centre
79 730 ADS228 Kent & East Sussex Railway K&ESR 90

Diagram: 24 **Built**: 1924 **Builder**: Eastleigh **Seats**: 64T **Dimensions**: 57′0′′ x 9′0′′

Built as loose coaches.

748 ADS229 Kent & East Sussex Railway
752 ADS70014 Isle of Wight Steam Railway Body only remains

CORRIDOR BRAKE THIRD BTK

Diagram: 213 **Built**: 1921 **Builder**: Eastleigh **Seats**: 32T **Dimensions**: 57′0′′ x 9′0′′

Built for use in five coach Bournemouth line pantry sets 431 – 434.

1282 3187 ADS179 Mangapp's Farm Railway Museum

Diagram: 135 **Built**: 1923 **Builder**: Eastleigh **Seats**: 32T **Dimensions**: 57′0′′ x 9′0′′

Built for use in five coach sets 435 – 440.

1353 3190 DS70016 TDW70016 Watercress Line

Diagram: 213 **Built**: 1923 **Builder**: Eastleigh **Seats**: 32T **Dimensions**: 57′0′′ x 9′0′′

Built for use in five coach sets 435-440.

1357 3193 ADS70133 Kent & East Sussex RailwayStored at Hoo Junction Yard

Diagram: 213 **Built**: 1925 **Builder**: Eastleigh **Seats**: 32T **Dimensions**: 57′0′′ x 9′0′′

Built for use in five coach Bournemouth line sets 441 – 444.

\- 3204 DS70085 West Somerset Railway

CORRIDOR FIRST FK

Diagram: 476 **Built**: 1924 **Builder**: Eastleigh **Seats**: 42F **Dimensions**: 57′0′′ x 9′0′′

Built as loose coaches.

\- 7200 ADS227 Kent & East Sussex Railway

RESTAURANT THIRD (with Kitchen) RT

Diagram: 592 **Built**: 1923 **Builder**: Eastleigh **Seats**: 29T **Dimensions**: 57′0′′ x 9′0′′

Built for use with five coach sets 435 – 440.

4151 7851 625S DS625 Watercress Line

▲ Pullman parlour first URSULA, one of two cars used as a restaurant at the Spot Gate, Mier Heath, Hilderstone, Staffs. This photograph was taken on 7th February 1987. *Peter Hall*

▼ Pullman Car No. 97, formerly CALAIS, converted to camping coach No. 9870 at the Old Marazion Station Holiday Centre, Cornwall on 10th April 1994. Note the six-wheeled bogies. *Stephen Widdowson*

▲ A line up of Pullman camping coaches at Marazion on 15th April 1994. These are Car No. 503 (ex AURORA), Car No. 502 (ex JUNO), ALICANTE, MIMOSA, Car No. 97 (ex CALAIS) and Car No. 154 (ex FLORA). These are now camping coaches 9878/2/4/69/70/1 respectively.
Stephen Widdowson

▼ DEVON BELLE, a Pullman observation car, in service at the Paignton & Dartmouth Railway on 27th May 1995.
Ivor Bufton

▲ GWR Collett Auto-trailer No. 174 at Bristol Bath Road on 6th June 1981 in departmental service prior to preservation. *Peter Hall*

▼ GWR Hawksworth Auto-trailer No 231 at Wallingford on 15th June 1968. This is now kept at the Didcot Railway Centre. *Bryan Hicks*

▲ GWR 'Toplight' corridor third No. 3898 at Winchcombe on the Gloucestershire–Warwickshire Railway on 11th December 1994. *Ivor Bufton*

▼ GWR special saloon No. 9001 at Loughborough on the Great Central Railway on 9th October 1994. Note the six-wheeled bogies. *Peter Fox*

▲ GWR Churchward nondescript saloon No. 9369 at Bridgnorth, Severn Valley Railway on 20th August 1986. *M.A. King*

▼ Hawksworth Dynamometer Car No. DW150192 at Didcot on 20th January 1996. This coach was built as corridor third 796 in 1948 and converted in 1962. *Ivor Bufton*

▲ GWR Siphon G No. 2790 at Lydney South Jn. on 21st January 1996. This coach is on the Dean Forest Railway *Ivor Bufton*

▼ All of the 'big four'railways had fleets of six-wheeled milk tanks which operated in special milk trains or often attached to the back of expresses. GWR 3043 in St. Ivel livery is seen at Toddington on 15th June 1996. *Ivor Bufton*

Two SR Maunsell-designed coaches at Sheffield Park on the Bluebell Railway on 29th September 1996. The coach pictured above is open third No. 1309 built 1935, whilst the one pictured below is corridor brake composite 6575 built in 1929. *Alex Dasi-Sutton (2)*

▲ SR Bulleid-design semi-open brake thrid No. 2515 at Sheffield Park on the Bluebell Railway on 29th September 1996. This coach which has two compartments and a four-bay open saloon was built after nationalisation in 1951. *Alex Dasi-Sutton*

▼ The Southern possessed large numbers of wooden four-wheeled parcels vans of which 1070, a parcels and miscellaneous van (PMV) seen at the Conwy Valley Railway Museum, Bettws-y-Coed on 28th January 1986 is a typical example. The CCTs (covered carriage trucks) were similar in appearance but had end doors, whilst the BYs (brake vans) had guard's facilities. *Ivor Bufton*

▲ HM The King's Saloon No. 798 was built by the LMS for HM King George VI at Wolverton in 1941. It is seen in the former National Railway Museum Annexe in 1986. *Peter Fox*

▼ LMS No. 592 is a third class sleeping car with seven four-berth compartments and was photographed at Llangollen on 7th January 1986. *Ivor Bufton*

▲ LMS period 1 corridor composite No. 3565 in use as a model railway club house at the former British Railways Staff Association at Aylesbury on 18th November 1989. This coach is an "all door" design, each compartment having its own door. The photograph is taken from the corridor side. *Peter Hall*

▼ LMS period 3 non-corridor third No. 11937 at the "Marsden Rattler" restaurant, South Shields on 8th April 1989. *Peter Hall*

Two LMS period 3 (Stanier) coaches in use at Bridgnorth, Severn Valley Railway on 12th October 1996. 26986 (above) is a corridor brake third whilst 12992 (below) is a corridor third. Both coaches were built after nationalisation. Note the "porthole" shape of the toilet window in 26986.

Hugh Ballantyne (2)

▲ The interior of LMS period 3 open third No. 27220 taken whilst in service on the Severn Valley Railway on 12th October 1996. *Hugh Ballantyne*

▼ BG No. 31420 is a typical LMS period 3 50′ vehicle, although built after nationalisation in 1950. It is seen on 13th October 1996, just after being repainted, at Kidderminster on the Severn Valley Railway. *Hugh Ballantyne*

▲ LNER Gresley-designed buffet car No. 643 (later renumbered 9131) at Highley Station, Severn Valley Railway in October 1984, restored to varnished teak livery. *Bryan Hicks*

▼ LNER Gresley open third No. 43600 (later 13354) at Bridgnorth, SVR on 17th October 1987. *Bryan Hicks*

▲ 1866 is an LNER Thompson-designed brake third. It was built in 1950 and numbered into the East Coast Joint Stock number series and was photographed at ICI Wilton on 12th March 1992 still carrying its departmental number DE 321120. It now resides at the Llangollen Railway.
T. Bye

▼ 88339 is one of two preserved lavatory composites. These coaches, designed by Thompson, were most unusual in being non-gangwayed coaches, but with side corridors leading to toilet compartments in the centre of the coach. The corridor on the first class end of the coach was on the opposite side to that on the third class end and thus each class had its own toilet. The idea was perpetuated by BR in some of their suburban designs. The coach is seen at Goathland on the North Yorkshire Moors Railway in April 1996. *P. Chancellor*

▲ 70470 is an LNER Gresely-design BGP and is seen at Oxenhope, Keighley and Worth Valley Railway on 11th May 1996. "BGP" stands for gangwayed brake van provided with shelves for pigeon traffic. *P.L. Pay*

▼ 70741 is a later design of BG and is now "Baggage Car No. 7" of the Venice Simplon-Orient Express set. It was photographed at Leamington Spa on 15th February 1983. *Bryan Hicks*

▲ The only remaining LNER "Quad-art" set, No. 74 at Holt on the North Norfolk Railway on 19th November 1994. *Ivor Bufton*

▼ LNER-design general utility van No. 1370 at the Conwy Valley Railway Museum, Betws-y-Coed on 28th January 1996. *Ivor Bufton*

3.2. SR PASSENGER-CARRYING STOCK

CORRIDOR THIRD TK

Order: 709 **Built:** 1934 **Builder:** Lancing/Eastleigh **Design:** Maunsell
Diagram: 2004 **Seats:** 48T **Dimensions:** 59'0'' x 9'0'' **Restriction:** 0

1020 DS70134 Kent & East Sussex Railway K&ESR No.59

OPEN THIRD TO

Order: 761 **Built:** 1935 **Builder:** Lancing/Eastleigh **Design:** Maunsell
Diagram: 2007 **Seats:** 56T **Dimensions:** 59'0'' x 9'0'' **Restriction:** 4

1309 081642 Bluebell Railway

Order: 706 **Built:** 1933 **Builder:** Lancing/Eastleigh **Design:** Maunsell
Diagram: 2005 **Seats:** 56T **Dimensions:** 59'0'' x 9'0'' **Restriction:** 4

1323 082232 ADS70266 Watercress Line
1336 081901 ADS70313 Bluebell Railway
1346 DS70201 083181 Kent & East Sussex Railway K&ESR No.78

THIRD CLASS DINING CAR RTO

Order: 98 **Built:** 1927 **Builder:** Lancing/Eastleigh **Design:** Maunsell
Diagram: 2652 **Seats:** 64T **Dimensions:** 59'0'' x 9'0'' **Restriction:** 4

Converted to Composite Dining Car in 1949. Seats: 24F 30T.

7866 1365 6802 7841 Bluebell Railway Formed in WWII Ambulance Train 68

OPEN THIRD TO

Order: 461 **Built:** 1930 **Builder:** Lancing/Eastleigh **Design:** Maunsell
Diagram: 2005 **Seats:** 56T **Dimensions:** 59'0'' x 9'0'' **Restriction:** 4

1381 ADS70175 Swanage Railway

Order: 3240 **Built:** 1947 – 48 **Builder:** Lancing/Eastleigh **Design:** Bulleid
Diagram: 2017 **Seats:** 64T **Dimensions:** 64'6'' x 9'0'' **Restriction:** 4

1456 DS70285 Bluebell Railway Part of National Collection
1457 DS70262 Swanage Railway

Order: 3581 **Built:** 1950 – 51 **Builder:** Lancing/Eastleigh **Design:** Bulleid
Diagram: 2017 **Seats:** 64T **Dimensions:** 64'6'' x 9'0'' **Restriction:** 4

1464 Bluebell Railway
1469 Keighley & Worth Valley Railway K&WVR No.5
1481 Bluebell Railway
1482 DS70314 Bluebell Railway

CORRIDOR THIRD TK

Order: 494 **Built:** 1931 **Builder:** Lancing/Eastleigh **Design:** Maunsell
Diagram: 2003 **Seats:** 64T **Dimensions:** 59'0'' x 8'6'' **Restriction:** 1

2356 081315 Bluebell Railway

Semi-open BRAKE THIRD BTso

Order: 3583 **Built:** 1951 **Builder:** Lancing/Eastleigh **Design:** Bulleid
Diagram: 2123 **Seats:** 48T **Dimensions:** 64'6'' x 9'0'' **Restriction:** 4

2515 Bluebell Railway
2526 082232, ADB975375 Venice Simplon Orient Express Stored at Eastleigh T&RSMD

CORRIDOR BRAKE THIRD — BTK

Order: 633 **Built**: 1932 **Builder**: Lancing/Eastleigh **Design**: Maunsell
Diagram: 2102 **Seats**: 48T **Dimensions**: 59'0" x 9'0" **Restriction**: 4

2768 ADS70172 Swanage Railway

Order: 498 **Built**: 1931 **Builder**: Lancing/Eastleigh **Design**: Maunsell
Diagram: 2105 **Seats**: 36T **Dimensions**: 59'0" x 8'0¾" **Restriction**: 0

3687 TDS70160 083409 Bluebell Railway
3690 ADS70163 Spa Valley Railway

Order: 489 **Built**: 1930 **Builder**: Lancing/Eastleigh **Design**: Maunsell
Diagram: 2101 **Seats**: 32T **Dimensions**: 59'0" x 9'0" **Restriction**: 4

3719 ADS70168 Bluebell Railway u/f only remains

Order: 487 **Built**: 1930 **Builder**: Lancing/Eastleigh **Design**: Maunsell
Diagram: 2101 **Seats**: 32T **Dimensions**: 59'0" x 9'0" **Restriction**: 4

3724 Bluebell Railway CWT Spray Coach CC99007

Semi-open BRAKE THIRD — BTso

Order: 3454 **Built**: 1950 **Builder**: Lancing/Eastleigh **Design**: Bulleid
Diagram: 2123 **Seats**: 48T **Dimensions**: 64'6" x 9'0" **Restriction**: 4

4008 ADS70251, 083641 Bluebell Railway

Order: 3249 **Built**: 1948 – 49 **Builder**: Lancing/Eastleigh **Design**: Bulleid
Diagram: 2123 **Seats**: 48T **Dimensions**: 64'6" x 9'0" **Restriction**: 4

4035 North Yorkshire Moors Railway
CWT Staff & Dormitory Coach CC99010
4036 Bluebell Railway
CWT Staff & Dormitory Coach CC99012 u/f only

Order: **Built**: 1947 – 48 **Builder**: BRCW **Design**: Bulleid
Diagram: 2124 **Seats**: 44T **Dimensions**: 64'6" x 9'0" **Restriction**: 4

4211 TDS70319 Watercress Line
4227 ADW150385 Bluebell Railway

Order: **Built**: 1948 – 49 **Builder**: BRCW **Design**: Bulleid
Diagram: 2125 **Seats**: 48T **Dimensions**: 64'6" x 9'0" **Restriction**: 4

4279 DS70248 Bluebell Railway

Order: 3240 **Built**: 1947 – 48 **Builder**: Lancing/Eastleigh **Design**: Bulleid
Diagram: 2123 **Seats**: 48T **Dimensions**: 64'6" x 9'0" **Restriction**: 4

4365 Swanage Railway RCT1 ARMY No.5200
4366 Swanage Railway ARMY No.5201
4367 Watercress Line ARMY No.5202

NONDESCRIPT OPEN BRAKE — BUO

Order: 708 **Built**: 1933 **Builder**: Lancing/Eastleigh **Design**: Maunsell
Diagram: 2654 **Seats**: 36U **Dimensions**: 59'0" x 8'6" **Restriction**: 1

4438 & 4444 converted to Ambulance Ward Cars in 1959. Seats: 11U (24 cots).

4432 Kent & East Sussex Railway K&ESR No.53
4438 7920 DB975279 Kent & East Sussex Railway K&ESR No.72
4441 082444 Bluebell Railway
4443 Kent & East Sussex Railway K&ESR No.54
4444 7921 AD777 Bluebell Railway

CORRIDOR COMPOSITE — CK

Order: 160 **Built**: 1928 **Builder**: Lancing/Eastleigh **Design**: Maunsell
Diagram: 2302 **Seats**: 16F 24T **Dimensions**: 59'0" x 8'6" **Restriction**: 1

5153 Kent & East Sussex Railway K&ESR No.55

Order: 498 **Built**: 1931 **Builder**: Lancing/Eastleigh **Design**: Maunsell
Diagram: 2304 **Seats**: 16F 18T **Dimensions**: 59'0" x 8'0¾" **Restriction**: 0

5600 TDS70155 Rother Valley Railway K&ESR No.91

Order: 495 **Built**: 1931 **Builder**: Lancing/Eastleigh **Design**: Maunsell
Diagram: 2302 **Seats**: 16F 24T **Dimensions**: 59'0" x 8'6" **Restriction**: 1

5618 Kent & East Sussex Railway K&ESR No.56

Order: 492 **Built**: 1930 **Builder**: Lancing/Eastleigh **Design**: Maunsell
Diagram: 2301 **Seats**: 24F 24T **Dimensions**: 59'0" x 9'0" **Restriction**: 4

5644 Bluebell Railway CWT Staff & Dormitory Coach CC99008

Order: 3235 **Built**: 1946 – 47 **Builder**: Lancing/Eastleigh **Design**: Bulleid
Diagram: 2318 **Seats**: 24F 24T **Dimensions**: 64'6" x 9'0" **Restriction**: 4

5761 Swanage Railway
5768 Bluebell Railway

CORRIDOR BRAKE COMPOSITE BCK

Order: 363 **Built**: 1929 **Builder**: Lancing/Eastleigh **Design**: Maunsell
Diagram: 2401 **Seats**: 12F 32T **Dimensions**: 59'0" x 9'0" **Restriction**: 4

6575 Bluebell Railway

Order: 799 **Built**: 1935 **Builder**: Lancing/Eastleigh **Design**: Maunsell
Diagram: 2403 **Seats**: 12F 32T **Dimensions**: 59'0" x 9'0" **Restriction**: 4

6686 Bluebell Railway
6697 Watercress Line CWT Spray Coach CC99011
6699 Swanage Railway CWT Spray Coach CC99009

CORRIDOR FIRST FK

Order: 376 **Built**: 1929 **Builder**: Lancing/Eastleigh **Design**: Maunsell
Diagram: 2503 **Seats**: 28F **Dimensions**: 59'0" x 8'0¾" **Restriction**: 0

7400 081621 Kent & East Sussex Railway K&ESR No.57

NONDESCRIPT SALOON UO

Order: 463 **Built**: 1931 **Builder**: Lancing/Eastleigh **Design**: Maunsell
Diagram: 2653 **Seats**: 42U **Dimensions**: 59'0" x 8'6" **Restriction**: 4

Note: Although described as "Nondescript", this coach was used for first or second class passengers, but not third class.

7798 DS70109 Kent & East Sussex Railway K&ESR No.58

RESTAURANT FIRST (with Kitchen) RF

Order: 635 **Built**: 1932 **Builder**: Lancing/Eastleigh **Design**: Maunsell
Diagram: 2656 **Seats**: 24F **Dimensions**: 59'0" x 9'0" **Restriction**: 4

Converted to First Class Kitchen, Buffet & Dining Car in 1947. Seats: 8F.

7864 Bluebell Railway

3.3. SR NPCCS (INCLUDING SECR PMVs)

Note: All BYs, CCTs and PMVs are 4-wheeled. All other vehicles have two four-wheel bogies unless otherwise stated. Widths quoted in this section are over handles.

PASSENGER BRAKE, NON-GANGWAYED BY

Order: 1091 **Diagram**: 3094 **Built**: 1941
Builder: Lancing/Eastleigh **Dimensions**: 36′0″ x 8′10⅞″ **Restriction**: 0

13 Swanage Railway

PASSENGER BRAKE, NON GANGWAYED B

Order: 1029 **Diagram**: 3093 **Built**: 1939
Builder: Lancing/Eastleigh **Dimensions**: 50′0″ x 8′9″ **Restriction**: 0

201		Spa Valley Railway	
205	083571	Tonbridge Model Engineering Society	
207		Steamtown Railway Centre, Carnforth	
219	083572	Mangapp's Farm Railway Museum	Body only remains
220	024450	Birmingham Railway Museum	
227		Dean Forest Railway	
232	ADB977065 083612	Swanage Railway	
242	083596	Wessex Traincare Ltd.	

Order: 3227 **Diagram**: 3093 **Built**: 1952–53
Builder: Lancing **Dimensions**: 50′0″ x 8′9″ **Restriction**: 0

256	Brighton Railway Museum
272	Nottingham Heritage Centre, Ruddington
273	Mangapp's Farm Railway Museum

Order: 927 **Diagram**: 3093 **Built**: 1937–38
Builder: Ashford/Eastleigh **Dimensions**: 50′0″ x 8′9″ **Restriction**: 0

385 Swanage Railway

PASSENGER BRAKE, NON-GANGWAYED BY

Order: 928 **Diagram**: 3092 **Built**: 1936–37
Builder: Ashford/Eastleigh **Dimensions**: 36′0″ x 8′10⅞″ **Restriction**: 0

404		Bluebell Railway
405	ADB975143	Gwili Railway
407		Conwy Valley Railway Museum
412	083356	Rutland Railway Museum
434	KDB975282	Grimsby & Louth Railway, Lugborough
435	ADB975672	National Railway Museum
436	ADB975140	Gwili Railway
440		Kent & East Sussex Railway
442		Bluebell Railway

Order: 974 **Diagram**: 3092 **Built**: 1938
Builder: Ashford/Eastleigh **Dimensions**: 36′0″ x 8′10⅞″ **Restriction**: 0

653 Bluebell Railway

Order: 974 **Diagram**: 3092 **Built**: 1938
Builder: Ashford/Eastleigh **Dimensions**: 36′0″ x 8′10⅞″ **Restriction**: 0

712 ADB975142 Derwent Valley Light Railway
Body only remains. Underframe used for NER 1214/2462.

Order: 1030 **Diagram**: 3092 **Built**: 1939
Builder: Ashford/Eastleigh **Dimensions**: 36′0″ x 8′10⅞″ **Restriction**: 0

765	Watercress Line	
798	Embsay Steam Railway	YDR No.20

Order: 1090 **Diagram**: 3092 **Built**: 1940–41

Builder: Ashford/Eastleigh **Dimensions:** 36'0" x 8'10⅞" **Restriction:** 0

931		Llangollen Railway	

PARCELS & MISCELLANEOUS VAN PMV

Order: 855 **Diagram:** 3103 **Built:** 1936 – 37
Builder: Ashford **Dimensions:** 36'0" x 8'10⅞" **Restriction:** 0

1070		Conwy Valley Railway Museum	
1074		Middleton Railway	
1108		Buckinghamshire Railway Centre	
1119		Kent & East Sussex Railway	Body only remains? U/F used for LCDR BT 49
1120	083268	Wessex Traincare Ltd.	
1125		Keighley & Worth Valley Railway	K&WVR No.107
1134	IOW1046 DS70256 082055	Isle of Wight Steam Railway	
1137		East Somerset Railway	
1145	DS70217	Kent & East Sussex Railway	K&ESR No.79
1152		East Anglian Railway Museum	
1153		Great Central Railway	

Order: 824 **Diagram:** 3103 **Built:** 1936
Builder: Ashford **Dimensions:** 36'0" x 8'10⅞" **Restriction:** 0

1162	DS149	Avon Valley Railway	
1168	KDS8	Caerphilly Railway	
1174	ADS70004	Severn Valley Railway	
1176	DS70056	Midland Railway Centre	
1184	DS164	Bluebell Railway	
1210	ADS796	Tanfield Railway	Body only remains. U/F used for ?
1213	DS70006	Kent & East Sussex Railway	
1218		Nene Valley Railway	Numbered 1587
1225		Kent & East Sussex Railway	Body only remains? U/F used for District Railway 100
1227		Dean Forest Railway	
1228	DS800	Kent & East Sussex Railway	U/F only remains, used for LC&DR 2947
1234	KDS3065	Swanage Railway	
1235	KDS13	Peak Railway, Darley Dale	
1240	ADS154	Spa Valley Railway	
1248	ADS161	Kent & East Sussex Railway	K&ESR No.80
1249	ADS160	Wales Railway Centre	

Order: 1031 **Diagram:** 3103 **Built:** 1939
Builder: Ashford **Dimensions:** 36'0" x 8'10⅞" **Restriction:** 0

1304		Keighley & Worth Valley Railway	K&WVR No.113
1312		Battlefield Steam Railway	ARMY No.47660
1314		Tanfield Railway	Body only remains. U/F used for MSLR 1509
1323	ADB975960 041468	Tanfield Railway	U/F only remains. Not yet re-used
1333		Battlefield Steam Railway	
1334		Great Central Railway	Body only remains at Loughborough Shed
1360		West Somerset Railway	
1367		Derwent Valley Light Railway	Numbered 1781
1375		Great Central Railway	Body only remains at Loughborough Shed
1391		East Lancashire Railway	
1396		East Somerset Railway	

COVERED CARRIAGE TRUCK CCT

Order: 3702 **Diagram:** 3101 **Built:** 1951
Builder: Ashford **Dimensions:** 36'0" x 8'10⅞" **Restriction:** 0

1418		Brecon Mountain Railway	Body only remains
1432		Steamport Railway Museum	
1439		East Anglian Railway Museum	
1449		Swanage Railway	

PARCELS & MISCELLANEOUS VAN — PMV

Order: | **Diagram:** 3103 | **Built:** 1951
Builder: Wolverton | **Dimensions:** 36'0" x 8'10⅞" | **Restriction:** 0

No.	Other numbers	Location	Notes
1458		West Somerset Railway	
1461		Hayling Island Railway Society	U/F only remains. Not yet re-used
1462		Tanfield Railway	Body only remains U/F used for GNR T 6032
1464		West Somerset Railway	
1470		Steamtown Railway Centre, Carnforth	
1497		Isle of Wight Steam Railway	Body only remains. U/F used for LC&DR C 6384

Order: 3229 | **Diagram:** 3103 | **Built:** 1947
Builder: Ashford | **Dimensions:** 36'0" x 8'10⅞" | **Restriction:** 0

No.	Other numbers	Location	Notes
1517		Keighley & Worth Valley Railway	Reduced to Crane Match Wagon
1533		Isle of Wight Steam Railway	Body only remains. U/F used for LC&DR BC IOW6369
1550		Keighley & Worth Valley Railway	Numbered S1470W. K&WVR No.114

Order: 3590 | **Diagram:** 3103 | **Built:** 1950
Builder: Ashford | **Dimensions:** 36'0" x 8'10⅞" | **Restriction:** 0

No.	Other numbers	Location	Notes
1562	ADB975997	Tanfield Railway	U/F only remains. Used for ?
1563		Battlefield Steam Railway	
1566		Isle of Wight Steam Railway	
1587		West Somerset Railway	Body only remains at Williton
1603		Isle of Wight Steam Railway	
1617		Isle of Wight Steam Railway	Body only remains U/F used for LBSCR T 2343

Order: 3590 | **Diagram:** 3103 | **Built:** 1950
Builder: Ashford/Lancing | **Dimensions:** 36'0" x 8'10⅞" | **Restriction:** 0

No.	Other numbers	Location	Notes
1633		West Somerset Railway	
1650		East Somerset Railway	
1669		Isle of Wight Steam Railway	

Order: 1659 | **Diagram:** 3103 | **Built:** 1943
Builder: Lancing | **Dimensions:** 36'0" x 8'10⅞" | **Restriction:** 0

No.	Other numbers	Location	Notes
1692	IOW1052 082975	Isle of Wight Steam Railway	
1698		Avon Valley Railway	Body only remains
1703		Foxfield Light Railway	
1706		Great Central Railway	
1711		Embsay Steam Railway	
1712		Avon Valley Railway	
1720	IOW1048 DS70257 082056	Isle of Wight Steam Railway	Body only remains. U/F used for LC&DR 653

COVERED CARRIAGE TRUCK — CCT

Order: 972 | **Diagram:** 3101 | **Built:** 1938
Builder: Ashford/Eastleigh | **Dimensions:** 36'0" x 8'10⅞" | **Restriction:** 0

No.	Other numbers	Location	Notes
1745	083286	Kent & East Sussex Railway	
1747	ADB975276 083523	East Lancashire Railway	
1750		Isle of Wight Steam Railway	Body only remains. U/F used for NLR FIRST 46
1765		Watercress Line	
1768		Watercress Line	
1770	024534	Chasewater Railway	

PARCELS & MISCELLANEOUS VAN — PMV

Order: 1191 | **Diagram:** 3103 | **Built:** 1942
Builder: Lancing | **Dimensions:** 32'0" x 8'10⅞" | **Restriction:** 0

1783	Isle of Wight Steam Railway	Body only remains. U/F used for LC&DR BS 45
1788	Bluebell Railway	Located at East Grinstead
1803	Isle of Wight Steam Railway	
1808	Kent & East Sussex Railway	K&ESR No.74

Order: 1092 **Diagram**: 3103 **Built**: 1940
Builder: Lancing/Eastleigh **Dimensions**: 32'0'' x 8'10⅞'' **Restriction**: 0

1834 024536	Northampton & Lamport Railway	
1851	Watercress Line	
1855	Bodmin Steam Railway	
1856	Bo'ness & Kinneil Railway	
1863	Gloucestershire-Warwickshire Railway	
1865 024742*	Midland Railway Centre	
1867	Middleton Railway	Converted to a coach
1874	Nottingham Heritage Centre, Ruddington	
1914	A.E.Knill & Co. Ltd., Barry Dock	

Order: 973 **Diagram**: 3103 **Built**: 1938
Builder: Ashford **Dimensions**: 32'0'' x 8'10⅞'' **Restriction**: 0

1925	Rutland Railway Museum
1930	Isle of Wight Steam Railway
1964	West Somerset Railway

Order: **Diagram**: 960 **Built**: 1919
Builder: Ashford (SECR) **Dimensions**: 32'0'' x 8'10⅞'' **Restriction**: 0

Designed and built by SECR. Prototype PMV.First number is SECR number.

132 1972 DS374 082757	Rother Valley Railway

COVERED CARRIAGE TRUCK CCT

Order: 3702 **Diagram**: 3101 **Built**: 1951
Builder: Ashford **Dimensions**: 32'4¼'' x 8'10⅞'' **Restriction**: 0

1991	West Somerset Railway	Body only remains at Williton

PARCELS & MISCELLANEOUS VAN PMV

Order: **Diagram**: 960 **Built**: 1922
Builder: Ashford (SECR) **Dimensions**: 32'0'' x 8'10⅞'' **Restriction**: 0

Designed and built by SECR. First number is SECR number.

152 1993 DS747	Gwili Railway	
153 1994 DS70031 DW70031	Bluebell Railway	
154 1995 DS792	Watercress Line	
155 1996 TDS70165	Mangapp's Farm Railway Museum	Body only remains
177 2012 ADS1035	Kent & East Sussex Railway	K&ESR No.89.

Order: 1659 **Diagram**: 3103 **Built**: 1943
Builder: Lancing **Dimensions**: 32'0'' x 8'10⅞'' **Restriction**: 0

2084	Middleton Railway	Converted to a coach

Order: 1191 **Diagram**: 3103 **Built**: 1942
Builder: Lancing **Dimensions**: 32'0'' x 8'10⅞'' **Restriction**: 0

2105	North Woolwich Old Station Museum	
2129 041493 DB975962	Tanfield Railway	Body only remains. U/F used for ?
2142	Bideford Station Museum	
2151	Midland Railway Centre	
2157	East Somerset Railway	
2158	Battlefield Steam Railway	

Order: **Diagram**: 3103 **Built**: 1934 – 35
Builder: Ashford **Dimensions**: 32'0'' x 8'10⅞'' **Restriction**: 0

2186 KDS150	Bluebell Railway

2188 KDS11 — Watercress Line
2196 DS93 — Watercress Line
2207 ADS70059 — Tanfield Railway — U/F only remains. Used for ?
2208 ADS70020 083608 — Wessex Traincare Ltd.
2213 ADS70154 — Avon Valley Railway
2216 ADS70140 083393 — Bluebell Railway — U/F only remains. Used for LBSCR 661
2223 CDS70025 041614 — East Lancashire Railway
2225 DS70156 — Tanfield Railway — Body only remains. U/F used for ?
2227 DS810 — Tanfield Railway — Body only remains. U/F used for ?

COVERED CARRIAGE TRUCK — CCT

Order: 3702
Builder: Ashford
Diagram: 3101
Dimensions: 32'4¼'' x 8'10⅞''
Built: 1951
Restriction: 0

2239 — Spa Valley Railway

Order: 277
Builder: Ashford
Diagram: 3101
Dimensions: 32'4¼'' x 8'10⅞''
Built: 1929
Restriction: 0

2276 CDS70202 — Bluebell Railway

GENERAL UTILITY VAN (GANGWAYED) — GUV

Order:
Builder: Ashford
Diagram: 3098
Dimensions: 51'3'' x 8'9''
Built: 1930 – 31
Restriction: 0

Underframe reclaimed from LSWR composite 3001 built 1905.

2339 DS70076 — Rother Valley Railway — K&ESR No.77.

COVERED CARRIAGE TRUCK — CCT

Order:
Builder: Ashford
Diagram: 3101
Dimensions: 32'4¼'' x 8'10⅞''
Built: 1931
Restriction: 0

2400 082949 — Wessex Traincare Ltd.

Order: 574
Builder: Ashford
Diagram: 3101
Dimensions: 32'4¼'' x 8'10⅞''
Built: 1932
Restriction: 0

2439 DS70324 — Northampton & Lamport Railway

GENERAL UTILITY VAN (GANGWAYED) — GUV

Order: 573
Builder: Ashford
Diagram: 3099
Dimensions: 53'3'' x 8'0½''
Built: 1931 – 32
Restriction: 0

Underframe of 2462 reclaimed from LSWR composite 2620 built 1910.
Underframe of 2464 reclaimed from LSWR brake third 2869 built 1905.
2464 was used in Sir Winston Churchill's Funeral train. Exported to USA in 1965.

2462 DS70141 — Bluebell Railway
2464 — Industry Halls Sheraton Resort & Conf. Centre, Los Angeles, CA, USA.

COVERED CARRIAGE TRUCK — CCT

Order:
Builder: Ashford
Diagram: 3101
Dimensions: 32'4¼'' x 8'10⅞''
Built: 1933
Restriction: 0

2497 ADS70264 — Kent & East Sussex Railway — U/F only remains. Used for LCDR 108

Order: 3764
Builder: Lancing
Diagram: 3101
Dimensions: 32'4¼'' x 8'10⅞''
Built: 1955
Restriction: 0

2504 — Brecon Mountain Railway — Body only remains
2524 — Brecon Mountain Railway — Body only remains
2527 ADB977010 — East Somerset Railway.
2530 — North Yorkshire Moors Railway
2531 — Bluebell Railway

FOUR-WHEELED SPECIAL CATTLE VAN — SCV

Order: 529 | **Diagram**: 3141 | **Built**: 1930
Builder: BRCW | **Dimensions**: 26′0″ x 8′10⅞″ | **Restriction**: 0

3716 DS70190 — Bo'ness & Kinneil Railway

Order: 3706 | **Diagram**: 3141 | **Built**: 1952
Builder: Lancing | **Dimensions**: 26′0″ x 8′10⅞″ | **Restriction**: 0

3733 — National Railway Museum

SIX-WHEELED MILK TANK — MILK

Order: 938 | **Diagram**: 3159 | **Built**: 1937
Builder: Ashford | **Dimensions**: 20′6″ x 8′4″ | **Restriction**: 0

Rebuild of 4-wheel built 1931, order 673, diagram, 3152.

4409 — Didcot Railway Centre

Order: 768 | **Diagram**: 3157 | **Built**: 1933
Builder: Lancing | **Dimensions**: 20′6″ x 8′4″ | **Restriction**: 0

4430 — Bluebell Railway

GENERAL UTILITY VAN — GUV

Order: 975 | **Diagram**: 3182 | **Built**: 1938
Builder: Ashford/Eastleigh | **Dimensions**: 50′0″ x 8′7¼″ | **Restriction**: 0

No.	Later No.	Location	Notes
4588	083361	Llangollen Railway	
4589		Nomix-Chipman, Horsham	Leaf Jetting Van CC99015
4590	083372	Gloucestershire-Warwickshire Railway	
4594		Swanage Railway	
4595		East Kent Light Railway	

Order: 3228 | **Diagram**: 3182 | **Built**: 1949
Builder: Lancing | **Dimensions**: 50′0″ x 8′7¼″ | **Restriction**: 0

No.	Later No.	Location	Notes
4598	083379	Nomix-Chipman, Horsham	
4600		Nomix-Chipman, Horsham	Spray Van CC99014
4601		Bluebell Railway	
4605	TDB975967	Isle of Wight Steam Railway	
4606	060957	Gwili Railway	

POST OFFICE SORTING VAN — POS

Order: 1043 | **Diagram**: 3192 | **Built**: 1939
Builder: Eastleigh | **Dimensions**: 58′0″ x 9′0″ | **Restriction**: 4

No.	Location	Notes
4920	Nene Valley Railway	Part of National Collection
4922	Bluebell Railway	

POST OFFICE STOWAGE VAN — POT

Order: 999 | **Diagram**: 3196 | **Built**: 1939
Builder: Lancing/Eastleigh | **Dimensions**: 58′0″ x 9′0″ | **Restriction**: 4

4958 — Watercress Line

PARCELS & MISCELLANEOUS VAN — PMV

Order: | **Diagram**: | **Built**: 19xx
Builder: | **Dimensions**: 32′0″ x 8′10⅞″ | **Restriction**: 0

Exact identities not known.

No.	Location	Notes
?	Pontypool & Blaenavon Railway	Body only remains
?	West Somerset Railway	Body only remains at Minehead
?	Wesssex Traincare Ltd.	Body only remains

4. LONDON, MIDLAND & SCOTTISH RAILWAY STOCK

4.0. INTRODUCTION

A considerable number of LMS items of coaching stock are in the hands of preservationists. Regrettably many of the passenger carrying types have been acquired direct from departmental service and require considerable restoration which in the majority of cases has still to commence. Fortunately however several later batches of passenger carrying vehicles were still in use on British Railways in the 1960s which allowed the Severn Valley Railway in particular to obtain carriages straight from service which continue to be used to this day. As with non-passenger carrying coaching stock of the other grouping companies much of this survived well into the preservation era, thus a fair number survive.

The definitive text on LMS design coaching stock is currently being updated, revised and expanded as a three volume epic and is strongly recommended being:-

The Illustrated History of LMS Standard Coaching Stock/David Jenkinson & Bob Essery, -Sparkford: Oxford Publishing Company, 1991- . (three volumes).

With such a reference for readers to consult historical information has been kept to a minimum in the following.

LMS passenger carrying coaching stock is referred to by three distinctive periods of design, these being used in this book. Period one covered the period 1923-1929/30, period two the period 1929/30-1932 and Period three the period from 1933 onwards. Period 1 coaches are high-waisted vehicles built entirely of wood and have either doors to every compartment and therefore three windows in each like non-corridor stock, or two windows per seating bay, one of which is a droplight. Period 2 coaches are wooden framed with either wood or steel cladding and have large picture windows, whilst period 3 coaches, often known as Stanier stock are wooden framed with steel cladding and have windows with radiused corners and sliding ventilators. As an exception to the above, certain period 1 coaches were built with large picture windows and two of these types are preserved. Full details of the design/construction of these periods are given in the first volume of the recommended text.

Carriages built before 1932 were numbered somewhat haphazardly in the gaps available between the various batches of pre-grouping coaches. In 1933 however a major renumbering took place which grouped all coaching stock into systematic number blocks according to coach type. This system persisted until the last LMS designed coaching stock was constructed in British Railways days. In this section preserved vehicles are listed numerically by this 1933 number, quite a number of the preserved vehicles were however constructed prior to this date and for these the earlier number is shown in the first column and the 1933 number in the second column. Where no pre 1933 number was allocated the first column is blank. Otherwise the layout of this section conforms to the rules given in 'Guide to Layout'.

4.0.1. PASSENGER STOCK

4.0.1.0. Sleeping Cars

Other than the Composite Sleeping Car examples of all the other designs of Sleeping Car are preserved.

The high number of post war survivors is due to many of these not being withdrawn until the 1970s, this number is however expected to reduce following the discovery of asbestos in some of the cars, indeed the West Somerset Railway has already disposed of Third Class Sleeping Car 615 for just this reason. The final First Class Sleeping Cars were withdrawn in the early 1970's and in 1971 eight of these were taken into departmental service as Civil Engineers Dormitory Coaches. Many of these being used for this purpose in connection with rebuilding the Menai Bridge. All but two of the preserved examples coming from these. The Third Class Sleeping Cars lasted a few years longer. The majority of those preserved see use as volunteer accommodation at their respective railways however special mention should be made of First Class Sleeping Car 395 which saw mainline use as part of Sir William McAlpine's private train in the 1970s.

The two pre-war convertible Third Class Sleeping Cars are of particular interest. These were built for the introduction of third class sleeping car accommodation on Anglo-Scottish services and were convertible for day and night use. The upper berths of the four in each compartment were folded back flush with the compartment partition during the day. They are one of the single-window period 1 designs referred to above. Both saw departmental service prior to preservation. 14241 has been fully restored at the National Railway Museum were it is normally on public display whilst 14452 is used for volunteer accommodation at Boat of Garten on the Strathspey Railway. From the early 1930s the LMS introduced purpose built sleeping cars for third class passengers and 592 is an example from this period it also being used for volunteer accommodation. In early British Railways days twenty five Third Class Sleeping Cars were built to twin berth layout and seven of these survive in preservation, regrettably as mentioned above, the presence of blue asbestos in these cars may result in the number reducing in coming years.

4.0.1.1. Royal Saloons

The LMS constructed three carriages specifically for Royal Train use, two of which survive. Following withdrawal in 1977 the two Saloons were transferred to the national collection and today can be normally found on public display. His Majesty the King's saloon is displayed at Kelvin Hall, Glasgow whilst Her Majesty the Queen's saloon is displayed at York. The third carriage was a support vehicle referred to as Sleeping, Brake and Power Car and was numbered 31209. Following withdrawal this carriage passed to Vic Berry Ltd., Leicester and although it was intended to retain this carriage it was broken up during 1991 following the company's financial collapse.

4.0.1.2. Gangwayed Side-Corridor General Service Stock

Carriages to five different layouts have been preserved, these being Corridor Third, Corridor Composite, Corridor Brake Third, Corridor Brake First and Corridor Brake Composite with all design periods being represented. Regrettably no Corridor Firsts are preserved. The majority of those preserved have seen departmental service and await restoration. It is however possible to travel on restored examples on the Severn Valley, Bo'ness & Kinneil and Straphspey Railways. Of particular note however is Corridor Composite 9229 which is located in the car park of the Aylesbury branch of the British Railways Staff Association were it is used as the associated Model Railway Club house. Special mention should also be made of Corridor Brake Third 27093 which now forms part of the national collection. Surprisingly this carriage was for many years stored at Craven Arms along with the Western Region mobile control trains. It has however not been established why it was there especially as it had no modifications. Not surprisingly this carriage was taken into the national collection when the mobile control trains were disbanded. It is currently on loan to the Midland Railway Centre. Also of particular interest are the two Corridor Brake Composites of lot 861, 6815 & 6839 which survive. These along with 6840 and similar 6869 from lot 1098 were converted by the Southern Region to Civil Engineers Staff & Dormitory coaches in 1966 taking numbers DS70244-247 and gave over twenty years such service in southern England. Regrettably 6840 and 6869 were scrapped a few years ago.

The only corridor brake first preserved bears little resemblance to how it emerged from Derby Works in 1927. In 1961 it was rebuilt as the LMR General Manager's Saloon and had its underframe replaced with a BR design one previously used on BS 43232. It took departmental number DM395707 at this time. In 1989 it was taken over by the Special Trains Unit of InterCity and renumbered 6320, it being used for various special workings. Following the sale of the assets of the Special Trains Unit in 1995, it became the property of Flying Scotsman railways Ltd. subsidiary company the Carriage & Traction Company Ltd. It now no longer sees main line use and is understood to be awaiting movement to the Weardale Railway should this project come to fruition.

4.0.1.3. Gangwayed Open General Service Stock

The principle design of this type preserved is the Open Third, however three First Class Dining Cars are also preserved. Only one of the pre war preserved examples has been restored so far, this being Open Third 9355 on the Severn Valley Railway which has been rebuilt as a Buffet Car and sees regular use. Of note however is that one of the Open Thirds, 6039, was one of the twenty converted to Steam Heat Generator Vans between 1958 and 1963. These were numbered 44401-44420 and remained in service until the early 1970s in capital stock and several for a few years longer in departmental service. Those transferred to departmental stock either retained their capital stock numbers with the addition of a 'DM' prefix or took departmental numbers in the range DM395938-940/947-950. 6039 has been restored in its Steam Heat Generator Van guise numbered 44408 and as such proves invaluable on the North Yorkshire Moors Railway. Regrettably the potential of two other vans, 44404 (ex 5806/8000) and 44414 (ex 5939/8023) was not realised by preservationists and they have recently been broken up at the East Lancashire Railway. A number of the post war Open Thirds were however purchased direct from BR service and it is possible to travel in these on the Severn Valley, Bo'ness and Kinneil and Foxfield railways. It is however possible to have a meal in 18358 at Dunkleys Restaurant, Castle Ashby.

The London Midland Region of British Railways had two of the previously mentioned mobile control trains and four of the six carriages converted for these in 1962 are preserved. All those preserved being Open Thirds numbers 7820, 7828, 7863 and 7868. Two of these were taken for inclusion in the National Collection whilst the others went for private preservation. 7863 from the National Collection has however recently been declared surplus and has been donated to the Midland Railway Centre along with the similar 8207. All four remain stored awaiting full restoration. The other two carriages formed in the trains which were regrettably scrapped were Corridor Thirds. These trains spent the majority of their time at Springs Branch near Wigan.

4.0.1.4. Non-Corridor General Service Stock

Five of these survive in preservation, all Thirds. Only 12066 at the Keighley and Worth Valley Railway can be savoured by passengers. 15486 and 11937 are effectively gutted with new interiors provided for their new roles as static restaurants whilst the other two await restoration.

4.0.1.5. Kitchen Cars

Two of these are in the hands of preservationists both having been substantially altered whilst in departmental service. 3286 was converted to a Track Recording Coach in 1956, a function which it performed until the mid 1980s. It currently awaits attention on the Watercress Line, obviously its rebuilding to original is unrealistic, however restoration in its departmental guise would be certainly sensible. 30088 was converted to an Inspection Saloon in 1958 and was used as such until the mid 1980s. It has now been restored and a adapted for use as a Camping Coach at Rowden Mill Station. At the same time Kitchen Car 30106 was converted to an Inspection Saloon numbered DM395280, this continues to see use with English, Welsh & Scottish Railway being based at Doncaster.

4.0.2. LMS NPCCS

4.0.2.1. Post Office Vans

Two Sorting Vans have been preserved both of which are displayed more or less in as withdrawn condition. Interestingly these two were withdrawn in the early 1970s when a considerable number of LMS design postal vehicles remained in service. Although final withdrawals did not take place until 1977 no further vehicles were saved.

4.0.2.2. Gangwayed Passenger Brake Vans

These were constructed to two distinctive designs, bogied and six-wheeled. The prolific bogied design continued in use until 1984 with several examples remaining in departmental service to this day. However from the early 1970s they were relegated to general parcels traffic and the majority had their gangways removed. Indeed of all those preserved only 31036 and 31359 are believed to have retained gangways. These vehicles have so far seen very little attention as regards restoration the majority being used for storage purposes. The distinctive six-wheeler design generally faired better than its bogied brothers with only 32991, 33004, 33005, 33006, 33007, 33017 having their gangways removed. Of these only 33007 remains intact at Steamport to represent this modification in preservation. The last four in service 32975, 32978, 32990 and 33004 were all withdrawn in the late 1970s and the three gangwayed of these passed for preservation. Of these 32975 has now been fully restored by the Bluebell Railway whilst 32978 and 32990 await restoration at their present homes. 32978 was formerly located at the Dean Forest Railway whilst 32990 was once at the Swanage Railway. The only other to have been fully restored so far is 33003 at the Strathspey Railway. 32988, 32991 and 32998 were initially restored complete but have subsequently had the body work removed due to poor condition and in time will all have ancient passenger bodies fitted. It is believed the underframe from 33002 has already been used in this way and now carries the body of GWR tri-composite 824 built in 1887.

4.0.2.3. Covered Carriage Trucks

Of the seven listed only one has so far seen any real preservation. This being 35062 at the Northampton & Lamport Railway which has been cosmetically restored. The other three which remain intact await restoration although they are all currently used for storage purposes as is the body of 8188 at the West Somerset Railway.

4.0.2.4. Motor Car Vans

These distinctive four wheel vans with the distinctive high arched roof latterly referred to as Covered Carriage Trucks were not finally withdrawn until the late 1970s. Consequently all but one went direct from service into preservation.

4.0.2.5. Theatrical Scenery Trucks

All three of the preserved examples are located at the Foxfield Railway. Although two are used for storage purposes one sees regular passenger use as a bar car in trains on this former industrial line.

4.0.2.6. General Utility Vans

Three of these extremely versatile vehicles have been preserved all of which saw departmental service following withdrawal. They were the first of the purely LMS design no-passenger carrying vehicles to display genuine 'passenger carriage' lineaments. The LMS actually referred to them as luggage and parcels vans, but latterly they were designated General Utility Van (GUV).

4.0.2.7. Fruit and Milk Van

The only example listed here is incomplete. Following withdrawal 40070 had its body work removed and for many years saw departmental service as a crane runner. It was initially preserved at the Strathspey Railway in this form, latterly however it has moved to the Tanfield Railway were it is having an ancient passenger body mounted on the underframe.

4.0.2.8. Fish Vans

Post War the LMS changed from using four wheeled vans for fish traffic to a more robust vehicle running on a very substantial six-wheel chassis. In spite of their traditional appearance, these vans made some concession to modern thinking in that the hardwood frame was mounted directly onto the chassis. The body frames were wood-sheathed inside and out thus providing an air cavity which offered a measure of thermal insulation. The sliding doors were similarly built and the roof was reinforced with steel carlines below the conventional board and canvas covering. The asphalt floor was arranged to 'fall' towards drains along the centreline to facilitate swilling out and interior walls were protected by varnish. The rapid erosion of rail-borne fish traffic soon made many surplus and many found further use as stores vans. The majority of those preserved having been used as such.

4.0.2.9. Horse Boxes

Only one example of a complete LMS design Horse Box has been preserved although the bodies of three others are now in the hands of preservationists. The complete Horse Box, 42608, is however worthy of special mention. This has been meticulously restored at the Midland Railway Centre and is now prominently displayed there as example of what can be achieved by preservationists. The bodies of LMS design horseboxs were often sold on as stables following withdrawal and although the locations of a few are listed later in the book it is believed that many others still exist.

4.0.2.10. Milk Tanks

Four LMS-design milk tanks have been preserved whilst a further one which latterly saw use as a Crane Runner minus tank is also preserved. As with the Southern Railway the earliest examples were built as four wheelers being subsequently converted to six wheelers. The three examples preserved from lot 1077 were all originally four wheelers. All were converted in 1937-38 to lot 1077 and treated as new vehicles rather than actual conversions. Of these three only 640 has been restored so far, however the other two remain complete awaiting attention. Of the other complete vehicles, 44057, has been fully restored and is normally on public display at the National Railway Museum, whilst 44044 has recently had some cosmetic attention. It will noted that all these four carried United Dairies Livery.

4.0.3. SALOONS & TEST TRAIN STOCK

4.0.3.1. Chaiman's Saloons

Regrettaby only one of the two Chairman's Saloons built in 1942 survives in preservation. They were built in 1942, although it is not known why they were allowed to be built during the war unless it was to act as mobile headquarters in connection with some aspect of wartime railway administration. In 1948 they were altered by the removal of the office facilities which were replaced with additional sleeping accommodation in 45005 and Sleeping/Catering accommodation in 45006. They continued to be used in this form until withdrawn, laterally being employed as Royal Train coaches. 45005 was the first to be withdrawn and was subsequently used on the mainline. It now is listed as being in the ownership of the Carriage & Traction Company, a subsidiary of Flying Scotsman Railways although continuing to reside at Carnforth. 45006 suffered the same fate as Royal vehicle 31209 mentioned earlier.

4.0.3.2. District Engineer's Saloons

Fourteen District engineers Saloons were constructed in the 1940s. Two of these have regrettably been scrapped but all the others remain with two still seeing use with English Welsh & Scottish Railway and one providing staff accommodation at York wagon repair depot. Two of the preserved examples were converted to Camping Coaches for use at Dawlish Warren in the early 1980s. In late 1995 one of these, 45044, was sold into private ownership and is now located at the former Fencote station which has been delightfully restored. The others are generally being well looked after at their new homes with restoration currently taking place to 45028 at Steamtown Railway Museum, 45036 at the Chinnor & Princess Risborough Railway, 45047 at the Midland Railway Centre and 45048 at the Gloucestershire-Warwickshire Railway.

4.0.3.3. Test Train Stock

A couple of purpose built carriages have been preserved as part of the National Collection although both still require restoration. Unfortunately the author has been able to discover few details regarding these two most interesting carriages at the time of going to press.

4.1. LMS PASSENGER-CARRYING COACHING STOCK

FIRST CLASS SLEEPING CAR — SLF

6-wheel bogies

Lot No.: 1570 **Built:** 1951 **Builder:** Wolverton **Period:** 3
Diagram: 2166 **Berths:** 12 **Dimensions:** 69'0" x 9'0"

-	378	DB975181	North Yorkshire Moors Railway	
-	379	DB975182	East Anglian Railway Museum	
-	380	DB975183	Great Central Railway	
-	381	DB975184	Watercress Line	

Lot No.: 1584 **Built:** 1951 – 52 **Builder:** Wolverton **Period:** 3
Diagram: 2166 **Berths:** 12 **Dimensions:** 69'0" x 9'0"

-	394		Strathspey Railway	SR No.179
-	395		Steamtown Railway Centre, Carnforth	
-	398	DB975188	Bluebell Railway	

THIRD CLASS SLEEPING CAR (convertible) — SLT(C)

Lot No.: 418 **Built:** 1928 **Builder:** Derby **Period:** 1
Diagram: 1709 **Seats:** 56T or 28 berths **Dimensions:** 60'0" x 9'0" **Type:** Single window.

14241	516	DM395777	National Railway Museum	

Lot No.: 428 **Built:** 1928 – 29 **Builder:** Derby **Period:** 1
Diagram: 1709 **Seats:** 56T or 28 berths **Dimensions:** 60'0" x 9'0" **Type:** Single window.

14452	531	DM395778	Strathspey Railway	SR No.177

THIRD CLASS SLEEPING CAR (four berth) — SLT

Lot No.: 699 **Built:** 1933 **Builder:** Derby **Period:** 3
Diagram: 1863 **Berths:** 28 **Dimensions:** 60'0" x 9'0"

-	592	DM395922	Llangollen Railway	

THIRD CLASS SLEEPING CAR (twin berth) — SLT(T)

Lot No.: 1574 **Built:** 1951 – 52 **Builder:** Derby **Period:** 3
Diagram: 2169 **Berths:** 22 **Dimensions:** 65'0" x 9'0"

-	603	Bluebell Railway	

Lot No.: 1628 **Built:** 1952 **Builder:** Derby **Period:** 3
Diagram: 2169 **Berths:** 22 **Dimensions:** 65'0" x 9'0"

-	612	Midland Railway Centre	
-	617	Swindon & Cricklade Railway	
-	621	Strathspey Railway	SR No.180
-	622	Bo'ness & Kinneil Railway	
-	623	Bluebell Railway	
-	624	North Norfolk Railway	

H.M. THE KING'S SALOON

6-wheel bogies

Lot No.: 1167 **Built:** 1941 **Builder:** Wolverton
Diagram: 2054 **Dimensions:** 69'0" x 9'0"

-	798	Glasgow Museum of Transport	Part of National Collection

H.M. THE QUEEN'S SALOON

6-wheel bogies

Lot No.: 1168 **Built**: 1941 **Builder**: Wolverton
Diagram: 2055 **Dimensions**: 69'0'' x 9'0''

-	799	National Railway Museum

SEMI-OPEN DINING FIRST RFso

These vehicles are unusual in having three 4-seat compartments and an 18-seat open saloon designated for dining. Dia. 1707 has wide single windows similar to those in period 2 vehicles.

Lot No.: 379 **Built**: 1928 **Builder**: Derby **Period**: 1
Diagram: 1707 **Seats**: 30F **Dimensions**: 57'0'' x 9'0'' **Type**: Single window.

15412 1023 ADM395205 East Lancashire Railway

Lot No.: 488 **Built**: 1930 **Builder**: Derby **Period**: 2
Diagram: 1719 **Seats**: 30F **Dimensions**: 57'0'' x 9'0''

10257 1030 DM395222 Midland Railway Centre

CORRIDOR THIRD TK

Lot No.: 9 **Built**: 1924 **Builder**: Derby **Period**: 1
Diagram: 1695 **Seats**: 64T **Dimensions**: 57'0'' x 8'10½'' **Type**: All door.

16782 1272 DM395584 Midland Railway Centre

Lot No.: 71 **Built**: 1924 **Builder**: Derby **Period**: 1
Diagram: 1695 **Seats**: 64T **Dimensions**: 57'0'' x 8'10½'' **Type**: All door.

1371 1295 KDM395498 024744 Peak Railway, Darley Dale

Lot No.: 95 **Built**: 1925 **Builder**: Derby **Period**: 1
Diagram: 1695 **Seats**: 64T **Dimensions**: 57'0'' x 8'10½'' **Type**: All door.

16243 1307 DM395812 Steamtown Railway Centre, Carnforth

Lot No.: 388 **Built**: 1928 **Builder**: Wolverton **Period**: 1
Diagram: 1695 **Seats**: 64T **Dimensions**: 57'0'' x 8'10½'' **Type**: All door.

14256 1428 DM395798 Northampton & Lamport Railway
14281 1451 DM395799 Midland Railway Centre

Lot No.: 551 **Built**: 1930 **Builder**: Derby **Period**: 2
Diagram: 1782 **Seats**: 56T **Dimensions**: 60'0'' x 9'0''

3030 1501 DM395801 Avon Valley Railway

Lot No.: 695 **Built**: 1933 **Builder**: Wolverton **Period**: 3
Diagram: 1860 **Seats**: 42T **Dimensions**: 57'0'' x 9'0''

- 1535 DM395832 Somerset & Avon Railway, Radstock

Lot No.: 801 **Built**: 1934 **Builder**: Wolverton **Period**: 3
Diagram: 1899 **Seats**: 42T **Dimensions**: 57'0'' x 9'0''

- 1782 DM395911 North Yorkshire Moors Railway

Lot No.: 1407 **Built**: 1946–47 **Builder**: Derby **Period**: 3
Diagram: 2119 **Seats**: 42T **Dimensions**: 57'0'' x 9'0''

- 2300 Severn Valley Railway

CORRIDOR COMPOSITE CK

Lot No.: 30 **Built**: 1924 **Builder**: Wolverton **Period**: 1
Diagram: 1694 **Seats**: 18F 32T **Dimensions**: 57'0'' x 9'0'' **Type**: All door.

8761 3515 ADM395470 Keighley & Worth Valley Railway

Lot No.: 120 **Built**: 1925 **Builder**: Wolverton **Period**: 1
Diagram: 1694 **Seats**: 18F 32T **Dimensions**: 57'0" x 9'0" **Type**: All door.

9229 3565 KDM395776 British Rail Staff Association, Aylesbury

Lot No.: 450 **Built**: 1930 **Builder**: Wolverton **Period**: 1
Diagram: 1716 **Seats**: 18F 32T **Dimensions**: 60'0" x 9'0" **Type**: Two window.

9389 3751 DM395802 Ystwth Valley Railway Stored at Old Oak Common CARMD

Lot No.: 531 **Built**: 1931 **Builder**: Wolverton **Period**: 2
Diagram: 1791 **Seats**: 18F 32T **Dimensions**: 60'0" x 9'0"

15509 3820 DM395815 Llangollen Railway

CORRIDOR BRAKE FIRST BFK

Lot No.: 326 **Built**: 1927 **Builder**: Derby **Period**: 1
Diagram: 1654 **Seats**: 27F **Dimensions**: 57'0" x 9'0"

18562 5033 DM395707 6320 Carriage & Traction Company Ltd.
Stored at Bounds Green T&RSMD

CORRIDOR BRAKE THIRD BTK

Lot No.: 859 **Built**: 1935 **Builder**: Wolverton **Period**: 3
Diagram: 1905 **Seats**: 24T **Dimensions**: 57'0" x 9'0"

- 5727 DM395895 East Lancashire Railway Reduced to underframe
- 5734 DM395898 Midland Railway Centre
- 5757 DM395867 Llangollen Railway

Lot No.: 898 **Built**: 1936 **Builder**: Derby **Period**: 3
Diagram: 1905 **Seats**: 24T **Dimensions**: 57'0" x 9'0"

- 5793 DM395903 East Kent Light Railway

Lot No.: 1035 **Built**: 1937 **Builder**: Derby **Period**: 3
Diagram: 1968 **Seats**: 24T **Dimensions**: 57'0" x 9'0"

- 5987 Steamtown Railway Centre, Carnforth Part of National Collection

CORRIDOR BRAKE COMPOSITE BCK

Lot No.: 31 **Built**: 1924 **Builder**: Wolverton **Period**: 1
Diagram: 1754 **Seats**: 12F 32T **Dimensions**: 57'0" x 9'0" **Type**: All door.

9884 6618 ADM395476 Southall Railway Centre

Lot No.: 208 **Built**: 1926 **Builder**: Wolverton **Period**: 1
Diagram: 1755 **Seats**: 12F 32T **Dimensions**: 57'0" x 9'0" **Type**: All door.

16411 6650 ADM395754 Llangollen Railway

Lot No.: 320 **Built**: 1927 **Builder**: Wolverton **Period**: 1
Diagram: 1755 **Seats**: 12F 32T **Dimensions**: 57'0" x 9'0" **Type**: All door.

18017 6678 ADM395758 Nene Valley Railway

Lot No.: 454 **Built**: 1929–30 **Builder**: Wolverton **Period**: 1
Diagram: 1704 **Seats**: 12F 32T **Dimensions**: 60'0" x 9'0" **Type**: Two window.

9864 6720 TDM395845 Peak Railway, Darley Dale

Lot No.: 861 **Built**: 1935 **Builder**: Wolverton **Period**: 3
Diagram: 1932 **Seats**: 12F 31T **Dimensions**: 62'0" x 9'0"

- 6815 DS70247 Peak Railway, Darley Dale
- 6839 DS70244 Avon Valley Railway

FIRST CLASS DINING CAR RFO

Lot No.: 734 **Built**: 1934 **Builder**: Wolverton **Period**: 3
Diagram: 1902 **Seats**: 42F **Dimensions**: 62'0" x 9'0"

- 7511 38740 Severn Valley Railway Latterly Exhibition Van

OPEN THIRD TO

Lot No.: 94 **Built:** 1924 **Builder**: Derby **Period:** 1
Diagram: 1353 **Seats:** 56T **Dimensions:** 57'0" x 8'10½" **Type:** Two window.

5861 7816 KDM395519 Midland Railway Centre Reduced to underframe
5913 7820 KDM395344 Buckinghamshire Railway Centre

Lot No.: 154 **Built:** 1925 **Builder**: Derby **Period:** 1
Diagram: 1692 **Seats:** 56T **Dimensions:** 57'0" x 9'0" **Type:** Two window.

16122 7828 KDM395345 National Railway Museum
16553 7863 KDM395346 Midland Railway Centre
16696 7868 KDM395347 Somerset & Avon Railway, Radstock

Lot No.: 185 **Built:** 1926 **Builder:** Metro. **Period:** 1
Diagram: 1745 **Seats:** 56T **Dimensions:** 57'0" x 9'0" **Type:** Two window.

5682 7991 M.S.C. 3 Midland Railway Centre
6039 8044 ADM44408 North Yorkshire Moors Railway Converted to Boiler Van

Lot No.: 302 **Built:** 1927 **Builder**: Derby **Period:** 1
Diagram: 1692 **Seats:** 56T **Dimensions:** 57'0" x 9'0" **Type:** Two window.

18358 8161 ADM395617 Dunkleys Restaurant, Castle Ashby

Lot No.: 343 **Built:** 1927 – 28 **Builder**: Derby **Period:** 1
Diagram: 1692 **Seats:** 56T **Dimensions:** 57'0" x 9'0" **Type:** Two window.

7878 8192 ADM395680 North Yorkshire Moors Railway
14718 8207 Midland Railway Centre

Lot No.: 431 **Built:** 1929 **Builder**: Derby **Period:** 1
Diagram: 1692 **Seats:** 56T **Dimensions:** 57'0" x 9'0" **Type:** Two window.

? 84XX ARMY 3322 MoD Long Marston Military Railway

Lot No.: 857 **Built:** 1935 **Builder**: Wolverton **Period:** 3
Diagram: 1915 **Seats:** 60T **Dimensions:** 57'0" x 9'0"

– 9125 KDM395892 Steamtown Railway Centre, Carnforth

Lot No.: 894 **Built:** 1936 **Builder**: Derby **Period:** 3
Diagram: 1915 **Seats:** 60T **Dimensions:** 57'0" x 9'0"

– 9205 ADM395923 Peak Railway, Darley Dale

Lot No.: 954 **Built:** 1936 **Builder**: BRCW **Period:** 3
Diagram: 1915 **Seats:** 60T **Dimensions:** 57'0" x 9'0"

– 9355 Severn Valley Railway SVR Buffet Car No. 149

THIRD (non-corridor) T

Lot No.: 231 **Built:** 1926 **Builder**: Newton Heath **Period:** 1
Diagram: 1700 **Seats:** 108T **Dimensions:** 57'0" x 9'0"

15486 10959 ADM395645 Dunkleys Restaurant, Castle Ashby

Lot No.: 523 **Built:** 1930 – 31 **Builder**: Derby **Period:** 2
Diagram: 1784 **Seats:** 108T **Dimensions:** 57'0" x 8'11¼"

12059 11406 DM395918 Bo'ness & Kinneil Railway

Lot No.: 1043 **Built:** 1937 **Builder**: Wolverton **Period:** 3
Diagram: 1906 **Seats:** 108T **Dimensions:** 57'0" x 9'0"

– 11937 DM395887 Marsden Rattler Restaurant, South Shields

Lot No.: 1094 **Built:** 1938 **Builder**: Wolverton **Period:** 3
Diagram: 1906 **Seats:** 108T **Dimensions:** 57'0" x 9'0"

– 12066 Keighley & Worth Valley Railway K&WVR No.6

Lot No.: 1633 **Built**: 1951 **Builder**: Wolverton **Period**: 3
Diagram: 2124 **Seats**: 108T **Dimensions**: 57'0" x 9'0"

–	12244	KDM395928	Keighley & Worth Valley Railway	

CORRIDOR THIRD TK

Lot No.: 1484 **Built**: 1949 – 50 **Builder**: BRCW **Period**: 3
Diagram: 2119 **Seats**: 42T **Dimensions**: 57'0" x 9'0"

–	12992		Severn Valley Railway	

CORRIDOR COMPOSITE CK

Lot No.: 1500 **Built**: 1949 – 50 **Builder**: Derby **Period**: 3
Diagram: 2159 **Seats**: 18F 24T **Dimensions**: 60'0¾" x 9'0"

–	24617		Severn Valley Railway	

Lot No.: 1586 **Built**: 1950 **Builder**: Derby **Period**: 3
Diagram: 2159 **Seats**: 18F 24T **Dimensions**: 60'0¾" x 9'0"

–	24725		Bo'ness & Kinneil Railway	

CORRIDOR BRAKE THIRD BTK

Lot No.: 1505 **Built**: 1949 – 50 **Builder**: Wolverton **Period**: 3
Diagram: 2161 **Seats**: 24T **Dimensions**: 57'0" x 9'0"

–	26880	DM395979	Severn Valley Railway	

Lot No.: 1506 **Built**: 1950 **Builder**: Wolverton **Period**: 3
Diagram: 2161 **Seats**: 24T **Dimensions**: 57'0" x 9'0"

–	26921		Severn Valley Railway	
–	26986		Severn Valley Railway	
–	27001		Peak Railway, Darley Dale	

Lot No.: 1575 **Built**: 1950 – 51 **Builder**: Derby **Period**: 3
Diagram: 2161 **Seats**: 24T **Dimensions**: 57'0" x 9'0"

–	27043		Strathspey Railway	SR No.128

Lot No.: 1597 **Built**: 1950 **Builder**: Wolverton **Period**: 3
Diagram: 2161 **Seats**: 24T **Dimensions**: 57'0" x 9'0"

–	27093		Midland Railway Centre	Part of national collection

OPEN THIRD TO

Lot No.: 1400 **Built**: 1945 **Builder**: Wolverton **Period**: 3
Diagram: 1999 **Seats**: 56T **Dimensions**: 57'0" x 9'0"

–	27109		Steamtown Railway Centre, Carnforth	Numbered 65830

Lot No.: 1401 **Built**: 1945 – 46 **Builder**: Wolverton **Period**: 3
Diagram: 1999 **Seats**: 56T **Dimensions**: 57'0" x 9'0"

–	27162	38746	Buckinghamshire Railway Centre	Latterly Exhibition Van
–	27218		Severn Valley Railway	
–	27220		Severn Valley Railway	
–	27234	38742	Strathspey Railway	Latterly exhibition van SR No.129
–	27249		Foxfield Light Railway	

Lot No.: 1402 **Built**: 1947 **Builder**: Wolverton **Period**: 3
Diagram: 1999 **Seats**: 56T **Dimensions**: 57'0" x 9'0"

–	27270		Severn Valley Railway	

Lot No.: 1438 **Built**: 1947 – 48 **Builder**: Wolverton **Period**: 3
Diagram: 1999 **Seats**: 56T **Dimensions**: 57'0" x 9'0"

–	27389		Bo'ness & Kinneil Railway	
–	27407		Bo'ness & Kinneil Railway	

4.2. LMS NPCCS

Note: All CCTs are 6-wheeled. All other vehicles have two four-wheel bogies unless otherwise stated.

KITCHEN CAR RK

Lot No.: 65 **Built**: 1924 **Builder**: Derby **Period**: 1
Diagram: 1697 **Dimensions**: 50'0'' x 9'0''

3286 30005 DM395223 Watercress Line

Lot No.: 956 **Built**: 1936 **Builder**: GRCW **Period**: 1
Diagram: 1912 **Dimensions**: 50'0'' x 9'0''

Modified for 'Coronation Scot' service.

– 30088 TDM395279 Rowden Mill Station, Herefordshire

POST OFFICE SORTING VAN POS

Lot No.: 1238 **Built**: 1939 **Builder**: Wolverton **Period**: 3
Diagram: 2043 **Dimensions**: 60'0'' x 8'7¼''

– 30225 Midland Railway Centre

Lot No.: 1559 **Built**: 1950 **Builder**: Wolverton **Period**: 3
Diagram: 2167 **Dimensions**: 60'0'' x 8'7¼''

– 30272 Nene Valley Railway Part of National Collection

PASSENGER BRAKE, GANGWAYED BG

Lot No.: 1096 **Built**: 1938 **Builder**: Wolverton **Period**: 3
Diagram: 2007 **Dimensions**: 50'0'' x 9'0''

– 30976 DB975562 Llangollen Railway

Lot No.: 1198 **Built**: 1939 **Builder**: Wolverton **Period**: 3
Diagram: 2007 **Dimensions**: 50'0'' x 9'0''

– 31036 095001 * Bo'ness & Kinneil Railway

Lot No.: 1261 **Built**: 1939–40 **Builder**: Wolverton **Period**: 3
Diagram: 2007 **Dimensions**: 50'0'' x 9'0''

– 31082 Keighley & Worth Valley Railway K&WVR No.111

Lot No.: 1304 **Built**: 1940–41 **Builder**: Derby **Period**: 3
Diagram: 2007 **Dimensions**: 50'0'' x 9'0''

– 31129 Steamtown Railway Centre, Carnforth
– 31148 East Kent Light Railway
– 31153 024417 Railcare, Wolverton Works

Lot No.: 1357 **Built**: 1941 **Builder**: Wolverton **Period**: 3
Diagram: 2007 **Dimensions**: 50'0'' x 9'0''

– 31217 Greater Manchester Museum of Science & Industry
– 31220 041618 ADtranz, Doncaster Works
– 31244 Birmingham Railway Museum
– 31255 Great Central Railway Body only remains at Loughborough Shed
– 31274 Bodmin Steam Railway Reduced to underframe
– 31281 Colne Valley Railway
– 31299 Midland Railway Centre

Lot No.: 1444 **Built**: 1947 **Builder**: Wolverton **Period**: 3
Diagram: 2007 **Dimensions**: 50'0'' x 9'0''

– 31343 Llangollen Railway

Lot No.: 1508 **Built**: 1949–50 **Builder**: Wolverton **Period**: 3
Diagram: 2171 **Dimensions**: 50'0'' x 9'0''

– 31352 Southall Railway Centre

–	31359	ADB975986	Battlefield Steam Railway	
–	31361	XDB977031	East Kent Light Railway	
–	31370	ADB975944	Great Central Railway	Body only remains at Loughborough Stn.

Lot No.: 1563 **Built**: 1949 **Builder**: Derby **Period**: 3
Diagram: 2171 **Dimensions**: 50'0" x 9'0"

–	31385	ADB977024 31402	East Lancashire Railway
–	31387	XDB977034	East Lancashire Railway

Lot No.: 1579 **Built**: 1950 **Builder**: Derby **Period**: 3
Diagram: 2171 **Dimensions**: 50'0" x 9'0"

–	31406		Dean Forest Railway
–	31407	XDB977037	Rail and Marine Engineering Ltd

Lot No.: 1588 **Built**: 1950 **Builder**: Wolverton **Period**: 3
Diagram: 2171 **Dimensions**: 50'0" x 9'0"

–	31420	XDB977023	Severn Valley Railway

Lot No.: 1359 **Built**: 1944 **Builder**: Wolverton **Period**: 3
Diagram: 2100 **Dimensions**: 57'0" x 9'0"

Note: These vehicles were built on second-hand underframes.

–	31926	Dunkleys Restaurant, Castle Ashby
–	31927	South Devon Railway
–	31930	Steamtown Railway Centre, Carnforth

PASSENGER BRAKE, GANGWAYED BGZ

These gangwayed six wheelers were fitted with coal stoves for use on trains without heating, e.g. milk trains, and were known as 'Stove R's by the LMS. They were coded 'STOVE BGZ' by BR if they still contained a stove.

Lot No.: 664 **Built**: 1932 **Builder**: Wolverton
Diagram: 1796 **Dimensions**: 31'0" x 8'6"

2884	32918	Midland Railway Centre
2886	32919	Severn Valley Railway

Lot No.: 1091 **Built**: 1938 **Builder**: Wolverton
Diagram: 2000 **Dimensions**: 31'0" x 8'6"

–	32975		Bluebell Railway	
–	32978		Great Western Museum, Coleford	
–	32988		Keighley & Worth Valley Railway	underframe only remains
–	32990		Somerset & Avon Railway, Radstock	
–	32991		Kent & East Sussex Railway	u/f only carries body of GER 197
–	32994		Cheddleton Railway Centre	
–	32998	DB975249	Midland Railway Centre	underframe only remains

Lot No.: 1262 **Built**: 1940 **Builder**: Wolverton
Diagram: 2000 **Dimensions**: 31'0" x 8'6"

–	33002	Didcot Railway Centre	Body only remains. U/f used for GWR 824
–	33003	Strathspey Railway	SR No.153
–	33007	Steamport Railway Museum	
–	33014	Buckinghamshire Railway Centre	
–	33016	Conwy Valley Railway Museum	

COVERED CARRIAGE TRUCK CCT

Lot No.: 111 **Built**: 1926 **Builder**: Wolverton
Diagram: 1871 **Dimensions**: 30'0" x 8'5¼"

8188	35054	CDM395489	West Somerset Railway	Body only remains

Lot No.: 123 **Built**: 1926 **Builder**: Wolverton
Diagram: 1871 **Dimensions**: 30'0" x 8'5¼"

5622	35062	CDM395492	Northampton & Lamport Railway
6589	35098	ADM395838	West Somerset Railway

Lot No.: 532 **Built:** 1930 **Builder:** Wolverton
Diagram: 1872 **Dimensions:** 30'0" x 8'5¼"

5657 35239 ? Telford Railway Centre

Lot No.: 594 **Built:** 1931 – 32 **Builder:** Wolverton
Diagram: 1872 **Dimensions:** 30'0" x 8'5¼"

4384 35289 DM395566 024379 Cheddleton Railway Centre

Lot No.: 746 **Built:** 1934 **Builder:** Wolverton
Diagram: 1872 **Dimensions:** 30'0" x 8'5¼"

– 35414 022199 Buckinghamshire Railway Centre
u/f only remains carrying body of LNWR (5)192

Lot No.: **Built:** 19xx **Builder:** Wolverton
Diagram: 187x **Dimensions:** 30'0" x 8'5¼"

? 35XXX ? Rutland Railway Museum SW 2
Exact identity not known

FOUR-WHEELED MOTOR CAR VAN MCV

Lot No.: 1154 **Built:** 1938 **Builder:** Met-Cammell
Diagram: 2026 **Dimensions:** 30'5" x 9'0⅞"

– 37011 St. Leonards Railway Engineering
– 37066 Nene Valley Railway
– 37071 Nene Valley Railway
– 37096 Nene Valley Railway
– 37103 ADM396003 West Somerset Railway
– 37141 Nene Valley Railway

Lot No.: GWR 1770 **Built:** 1956 – 57 **Builder:** Swindon
Diagram: 2026 **Dimensions:** 30'5" x 9'0⅞"

– 37207 Dean Forest Railway
– 37221 Sail & Steam Engineering Ltd Body only remains
– 37222 Ilderton Station House Cafe & Restaurant
– 37224 Keighley & Worth Valley Railway K&WVR No. 109. u/f only remains
– 37225 Great Central Railway

Lot No.: 1636 **Built:** 1951 – 52 **Builder:** Earlestown
Diagram: 2026 **Dimensions:** 30'5" x 9'0⅞"

– 37306 Tanfield Railway Body only remains, u/f not yet used
– 37308 Tanfield Railway Body only remains, u/f not yet used
– 37311 Keighley & Worth Valley Railway K&WVR No.110
– 37326 Northampton & Lamport Railway

THEATRICAL SCENERY TRUCK TST

Lot No.: 160 **Built:** 1925 – 26 **Builder:** Derby
Diagram: 1875 **Dimensions:** 42'5" x 8'5¼"

46 37508 Foxfield Light Railway

Lot No.: 308 **Built:** 1927 **Builder:** Derby
Diagram: 1882 **Dimensions:** 42'5" x 8'5¼"

4700 37518 Foxfield Light Railway
4714 37519 Foxfield Light Railway 'The Bass Belle'

GENERAL UTILITY VAN GUV

Lot No.: 848 **Built:** 1935 **Builder:** Derby
Diagram: 1870 **Dimensions:** 42'0" x 8'6"

– 37817 TDB975229 Bo'ness & Kinneil Railway

Lot No.: 864 **Built**: 1935 **Builder**: Wolverton
Diagram: 1870 **Dimensions**: 42′0″ x 8′6″

–	37882	ADB975241	Scottish Industrial Railway Centre	

Lot No.: 1050 **Built**: 1937 **Builder**: Wolverton
Diagram: 1870 **Dimensions**: 42′0″ x 8′6″

–	37909	ADB975560	Caledonian Railway	

FRUIT AND MILK VAN — FMV

Six-wheeled.

Lot No.: 223 **Built**: 1926 **Builder**: Wolverton
Diagram: 1873 **Dimensions**: 30′5″ x 8′5¼″

3826	40070	ADM395663	Tanfield Railway	u/f only remains used for MR ?

FISH VAN — FISH

Six-wheeled.

Lot No.: 1428 **Built**: 1946 – 47 **Builder**: Wolverton
Diagram: 2115 **Dimensions**: 31′0″ x 8′0″

–	40212	ADM40212 024510	West Somerset Railway	
–	40226		Bo'ness & Kinneil Railway	

Lot No.: 1445 **Built**: 1949 **Builder**: Wolverton
Diagram: 2115 **Dimensions**: 31′0″ x 8′0″

–	40252	ADM40252	Peak Railway, Darley Dale	Locked in Matlock station shed
–	40284		Nene Valley Railway	
–	40288	ADM40288	Derwent Valley Light Railway	Body only remains
–	40294	ADM40294	Peak Railway, Darley Dale	

Lot No.: 1509 **Built**: 1949 **Builder**: Wolverton
Diagram: 2115 **Dimensions**: 31′0″ x 8′0″

–	40311	ADM40311	Derwent Valley Light Railway	Body only remains
–	40320	ADM40320	Southall Railway Centre	
–	40326	ADM40326 024512	West Somerset Railway	

Lot No.: 1452 **Built**: 1948 **Builder**: Derby
Diagram: 2125 **Dimensions**: 21′0″ x 8′6½″

Four-wheeled

–	4258X		Fransham Station, Norfolk	Body only remains
	4258X		Bo'ness & Kinneil Railway	Body only remains

HORSE BOX — HB

Four-wheeled.

Lot No.: 1534 **Built**: 1948 – 49 **Builder**: Derby
Diagram: 2125 **Dimensions**: 21′0″ x 8′6½″

–	42598		Mid-Suffolk Light Railway, Brockford	Body only remains
	42608		Midland Railway Centre	

MILK TANK — MILK

Six-wheeled.

Lot No.: 1077 **Built**: 1937 – 38 **Builder**: Derby
Diagram: 1993 **Capacity**: 3000 gallons **Dimensions**: 20′6″ x 7′9″

638	44000	ADW44000 041499	Carriage & Traction Company Ltd	United Dairies Tank. Stored at Ferme Park CS
640	44002	ADW44002	Keighley & Worth Valley Railway	United Dairies Tank
5289	44018	ADW44018 041961	Midland Railway Centre	United Dairies Tank
5364	44019	ADW44019 041882	Midland Railway Centre	United Dairies Tank

Lot No.: 812 **Built**: 1934 **Builder**: Derby
Diagram: 1994 **Capacity**: 3000 gallons **Dimensions**: 20'6'' x 7'9''

– 44044 ADW44044 East Somerset Railway United Dairies Tank

Lot No.: 1067 **Built**: 1937 **Builder**: Derby
Diagram: 1994 **Capacity**: 3000 gallons **Dimensions**: 20'6'' x 7'9''

– 44057 National Railway Museum United Dairies Tank

Lot No.: 631 **Built**: 1931 **Builder**: Derby
Diagram: 1994 **Dimensions**: 20'6'' x 7'9''

6093 44180 ADM395780 Midland Railway Centre Reduced to Crane Runner

4.3. LMS SALOONS & DEPARTMENTAL VEHICLES

CHAIRMAN'S SALOON

Lot No.: 1323 **Built**: 1942 **Builder**: Wolverton
Diagram: 2066 **Dimensions**: 60'0" x 9'0"

Rebuilt to diagram 2136 in 1948

–	45005	Steamtown Railway Centre, Carnforth	

DISTRICT ENGINEER'S SALOON

Lot No.: 1356 **Built**: 1944 **Builder**: Wolverton
Diagram: 2046 **Dimensions**: 50'0" x 9'0"

–	45021	Strathspey Railway	SR No.130

Lot No.: 1327 **Built**: 1942 **Builder**: Wolverton
Diagram: 2046 **Dimensions**: 50'0" x 9'0"

–	45028	Great Central Railway	Under restoration at Steamtown, Carnforth

Lot No.: 1432 **Built**: 1947 **Builder**: Wolverton
Diagram: 2046 **Dimensions**: 50'0" x 9'0"

–	45036	Chinnor & Princess Risborough Railway	

Lot No.: 1221 **Built**: 1940 **Builder**: Wolverton
Diagram: 2046 **Dimensions**: 50'0" x 9'0"

–	45044	Fencote Old Stn., Herefordshire	Camping Coach 'Cardiff'
–	45045	Llangollen Railway	

Lot No.: 1264 **Built**: 1941 **Builder**: Wolverton
Diagram: 2046 **Dimensions**: 50'0" x 9'0"

–	45046	Dawlish Warren Camp Site	Camping Coach 'Plymouth'
–	45047	Midland Railway Centre	
–	45048	Gloucestershire-Warwickshire Railway	

TEST TRAIN STOCK

Lot No.: **Built**: 1949 **Builder**:
Diagram: **Dimensions**: ' " x ' "

Dynamometer Car No.3

–	45049	East Lancashire Railway	Part of National Collection

Lot No.: **Built**: 1938 **Builder**:
Diagram: **Dimensions**: ' " x ' "

Mobile Brake Unit No.1

–	45053 ADM45053M	National Railway Museum	Test Unit

5. LONDON & NORTH EASTERN RAILWAY STOCK

5.0 INTRODUCTION

Many readers will be familiar with the distinctive Gresley Buffet Cars which outlived all other grouping day time passenger carrying stock by many years. In 1972 their were still ten of these in regular service, all of which are now preserved, the last not being withdrawn until 1977. Otherwise the vast majority of the seventy or so preserved passenger carrying carriages have come from departmental service. This and the predominant use of wood in the body construction has obviously contributed to the fact that very few have as yet been fully restored which in turn limits opportunities to savour travel in these vehicles. Study of the list of preserved vehicles will indicate how few are preserved in proportion to those constructed especially as several very similar vehicles are represented. Just as with Steam Locomotives London & North Eastern Railway (LNER) carriages are poorly represented in preservation.

For those wishing to read further about London & North Eastern Railway carriages the author strongly recommends the recently published:-

LNER Carriages/Michael Harris.-Nairn:Thomas & Lochar, 1994.

As such a comprehensive text now exists it is not the intention to dwell here on the history and description of the preserved vehicles, however a few brief notes are given.

5.0.1. NUMBERING

The numbering schemes adopted by the LNER were subject to frequent change, particularly in the early years. New coaches were allocated the next available number in separate series for the various sections of the LNER. When a coach was transferred from one section to another, e.g. from the North Eastern section to the Great Central section, it had to be renumbered. Thus the painted number of the vehicle gave no indication whatsoever of its type!

From 1943 however a logical scheme was introduced. The East Coast Joint Stock (ECJS) series was kept for coaches operating on the Kings Cross-Newcastle-Scotland services and coaches in this series were generally not renumbered, although some were transferred out of this series at this stage. The ECJS range was 1-1999, Gangwayed passenger-carrying stock was numbered in the range 9000-18999, Passenger Brakes and vans in the range 70000-70999 and non-gangwayed passenger-carrying coaching stock in the range 80000-88999. Short length Great Eastern section non-corridor stock numbered in the 6xxxx serise was not renumbered and neither were pre-grouping carriages. In addition a separate numbering scheme existed for various items of non-passenger-carrying coaching stock. In this section, vehicles are listed numerically by their 1943 number conveniently grouping them together by types. The non-passenger-carrying coaching stock items appear in a separate section at the end.

One carriage included here would perhaps be better covered in a book covering preserved North Eastern Railway carriages. Open Third 2945 is one of two ordered by the North Eastern Railway but actually constructed by the LNER before the latter had established its standard carriage design. It was not renumbered in 1943 as it was numbered in the pre-grouping series. Following withdrawal in 1958 it saw departmental service as a Work Study Mobile Office, it is now undergoing progressive restoration at the North Yorkshire Moors Railway.

5.0.2. PASSENGER-CARRYING COACHING STOCK

5.0.2.1. Gresley Stock

The only surviving example of Gresley articulated stock is the Quad-art set preserved on the North Norfolk Railway. Quad-art sets were made up of four teak bodied coaches with the emphasis on high capacity, the preserved example being designated for use on Great Northern suburban services. Normally two sets would form an eight coach train and the high capacity making them particularly popular with the operating department. The preserved set was built to a GNR design, noticeable by the lack of ventilators to the doors and typical Great Northern style guards lookouts. For many years the set was the mainstay of services on the North Norfolk Railway, which along with the exposure to the salty North Sea air has taken its toll, it now being stored pending a major restoration.

The standard LNER corridor carriage design was finalised in late 1923, using a 60′ underframe. This was in advance of other grouping carriages at the time by virtue of the Pullman gangways and buckeye couplers. The wooden teak-panelled body with squared mouldings and windows was more traditional than modern, particularly as the LNER persisted with this construction until 1942. All these standard coaches were mounted on the excellent Gresley double-bolster bogies.

The vast majority of Gresley stock preserved are Third Class vehicles with just one Corridor Composite, two Corridor Brake Composites and a Corridor Brake First representing First Class accommodation. Corridor Composite 18033 saw departmental service as a Civil Engineers Staff Coach, it now being used as a static members club coach at the Great Central Railway. Corridor Brake Composite 10078 is one of several LNER carriages now restored and running on the Severn Valley, the only railway currently able to turn out a rake of such stock. The other Corridor Brake Composite 10021 is also restored but in its departmental guise as a Staff and Tool Van on the North Yorkshire Moors Railway. Although a late arrival in the ranks of preserved LNER carriages Corridor Brake First 11047 is currently the focus of considerable attention at the Stephenson Railway Museum and hopefully it will not be too long before it can be savoured on the associated North Tyneside Steam Railway.

Mention should be made at this point regarding the re-occurring theme of mobile control trains. No fewer than twenty four of the forty eight carriages converted for these were of LNER design. Regrettably however the opportunity was missed some what when these vehicles became available with only thirteen being preserved. Unlike the English based trains vehicles in the Scottish pair of trains were not given departmental numbers thus it may not be immediately apparent that Corridor Third 12934 at the Buckinghamshire Railway Centre, Open Third 13251 at the East Anglian Railway Museum and Open Third 13254 at the North Yorkshire Moors Railway were formerly departmental coaches. These three being the only survivors of the eight carriages used in the Scottish trains which were latterly located at Carstairs. The other sixteen carriages were formed in eastern region trains of which the final locations were Heaton, York Clifton Carriage Shed and Doncaster were two trains were kept. One carriage only has been preserved from the Heaton train, this being Open Third 13320 which is currently undergoing a very thorough restoration on the North Yorkshire Moors Railway. In contrast only one carriage from the York train was scrapped. Two Open Thirds from this train, 13317 and 13354 went to the Severn Valley were the former has now entered passenger service whilst restoration progresses on the later. The other survivor from the train, 12322, has had a rather interesting subsequent history. It initially went to Steamtown Railway Centre at Carnforth. Following several years storage it was extensively rebuilt for use as a dining carriage in the luxuriant 'Royal Scotsman' train. Regrettably it suffered collision damage in 1992 which meant it would not be possible to be used again on the mainline. However the damage was not as severe as this may imply and it has now moved to the North Yorkshire Moors Railway following a period of storage at the premises of Lancastrian Carriage and Wagon at Heysham. Six of the eight carriages based at Doncaster have gone for preservation. Three Open Thirds 13385, 13407 and 13548 have been preserved at the Embsay Steam Railway were restoration progresses slowly. A further Open Third, 13547 has been returned to service at the Severn Valley Railway. The other two to be preserved were Corridor Thirds 12481 and 12328, both these are now under going restoration for eventual use on the North Yorkshire Moors Railway the later currently being located at Steamtown Railway Centre, Carnforth were restoration is being professionally carried out as funds permit.

In contrast to the large number of corridor carriages of Gresley design only five example of non-corridor design have been preserved. The most interesting of these is Dukinfield built Lavatory Composite 88026 which latterly saw use as a Civil Engineers Staff and Tool Coach. It currently serves a similar function at the Derwent Valley Railway.

Almost certainly the most spectacular Gresley carriages constructed were the two Coronation Observation Saloons. These being the only remaining vehicles of those constructed for the 'Silver Jubilee', 'Coronation' and 'West Riding Limited'. The 'Coronation' ran as a nine coach train, four articulated twins and the observation saloon, although the later was included in the train during the summer months only. These saloons are 51′ 9″ in length with the most distinctive feature being that one end slops downwards in matching shape to the front end of the 'A4' streamlined Pacific locomotives. The interior seated 16 in large armchairs. At the train end of the coach was a compartment for letter mails. The 'Coronation' stock was stored from 1940 and all except the observation saloons reappeared from 1948. The observation saloons were used occasionally until 1956, when 1729 commenced regular summer service on the West Highland line, to be joined later by 1719, they continued to be used on this route until the end of the 1967 summer season. Both were rebuilt in 1959 with a more angular observation end which provided better viewing. Preservation has not been as kind to the pair as one would hope, 1719 is currently stored on the Great Central Railway awaiting restoration whilst 1729 has remained in a part restored condition at Steamtown, Carnforth for many years, a plan to reinstate its original end appearing to have been abandoned mid way through.

Twelve of the distinctive Gresley design Restaurant Buffet Cars have been preserved of the twenty five built to diagram 167. The original car 9126 (32372) was built with a gas stove but the remainder were all electric. They originally saw service on a variety of workings which following a review of catering provision either had restaurant cars replaced with buffet cars or had catering provided for the first time. Preservation has served many of the cars well with many being used for the intended purpose. Special mention should however be made of those which have gone through thorough restoration amongst which, 641 on the North Yorkshire Moors Railway, 643 on the Severn Valley Railway, 650 at the National Railway Museum, 24280 on the Great Central Railway and 51769 on the North Norfolk Railway are restored in teak livery. In addition several others are progressively being restored.

Two similar carriages were also built in 1939 to diagram 275 numbered 9195 and 9196 these being a hybrid between a buffet and a restaurant car. The kitchen which had all electric cooking was at one end, next came the counter, then a section for buffet passengers with eighteen tip-up seats, finally a dining section with twelve seats at tables with lamps. The saloons were divided by acrylic screens in aluminium framing. The carriages were originally intended for use between York and Swindon on the Aberdeen-Penzance service. The survivor 9195 was rebuilt by BR with a modernised interior and gas cooking not being withdrawn until 1973. Following a spell of main line use it now serves as a static refreshment car at Steamtown Railway Centre, Carnforth.

1938 saw the construction of two Restaurant Lounge Buffet cars for use on the Flying Scotsman numbered 1852 and 1853. The interiors were unique in that the lounge area was partitioned off by a glass screen. At one end was a buffet/bar area installed with electric cooking, at the other a ladies retiring room. The two cars ran in the 'Flying Scotsman' sets for ten years before being replaced by more modern vehicles. In 1959 both coaches were rebuilt as conventional buffet cars and equipped with gas cooking equipment. The survivor, 1852 was withdrawn in 1965 and following various moves is now located at the Great Central Railway were following several years service it has been retired in order to allow further restoration work to take place.

Several Gresley design Restaurant cars are also now preserved all having seen departmental service following withdrawal. Restaurant Firsts 9002, 9007 and 9019 are examples of the standard LNER design with kitchen and pantry, 9002 was originally fitted with gas cooking whilst the others were installed with electric cooking from new. 9162 is of particular interest being one of a small number of Restaurant Composite carriages constructed for use in Scotland with electric cooking. In 1961 it had propane gas cooking equipment installed. Following a period in departmental service as a Civil Engineers staff coach it has been preserved at the Severn Valley Railway were restoration is progressing slowly.

Only two LNER Sleeping Cars are now preserved in Great Britain, the menace of blue asbestos having curtailed the existence of several others in the past few years. Both the survivors are of Gresley design and are used for volunteer accommodation on their respective railways. Mention should however be made of the two First Class Sleeping Cars exported to the National Railroad Museum, Green Bay, Wisconsin, United States of America in 1969. These cars were built in 1936 however in1944 1592 was converted at Doncaster for use by General Eisenhower as his personal carriage named 'Bayonet'. The exterior was entirely armour-plated and shutters were fitted to the windows. Six of the berths were replaced by a conference room and Eisenhower's personal sleeping and dressing room. The conference room was equipped with a desk, table and chairs. In post-war days 1592 was rebuilt to its former state as a sleeping car and survived in service until 1966. 1591 & 1592 were then restored at Doncaster with 1592 being returned to its wartime style prior to export.

Although the standard length of Gresley stock was 61' 6", shorter vehicles of 52' 6" were constructed for use on Great Eastern lines radiating from London Liverpool Street. Four carriages of this length have now been preserved. These carriages kept their original numbers in the 6xxxx series as stated earlier. Open Thirds 60505 and 60525 are both stored at Steamtown Railway Centre, Carnforth prior to movement to their eventual destinations. 60505 along with GNR BTK 1798 have been cosmetically restored by Carnforth Railway Restoration and Engineering Services and are intended to be moved to Leader Foot near Galashiels as static exhibits at a heritage centre being developed around the historic viaduct. At the time of writing planning difficulties are holding up progress with this project. 60525 has only recently entered the ranks of preserved carriages. It is eventually intended that it will be restored at the North Yorkshire Moors Railway. Corridor Third 61634 and Corridor Brake Third 62565 await restoration at their current homes.

Another Gresley design well represented in preservation is the Gangwayed Passenger Full Brake, several of which were fitted with shelves to allow the conveyance of pigeons. Eleven of these distinctive bogie carriages are now preserved although several others have been broken up to provide parts for other preserved Gresley carriages. The majority of the preserved examples were built to diagram 245 and those remaining on bogies are generally in complete condition although only 70470 on the Keighley & Worth Valley Railway has seen substantial restoration so far. The one without bogies, 70460, saw departmental service as a Breakdown Train Tool Van and is now used as a store/ workshop at Steamtown Carnforth. 70491 was one of three, the other two being to Thompson design and also preserved, which formed a Safety Exhibition Train, it now been used for storing track materials at Carrog on the Llangollen Railway. Of particular note is 70741 which is the only preserved example built to diagram 260. This was extensively restored for use as the original luggage van in the Venice-Simplon Orient Express set, a duty it undertook until being retired in 1994. It is now in temporary use as a store at the Stewarts Lane depot of the Venice-Simplon Orient Express. The earliest preserved example 70268 was converted to a Post Office Tender Van and in this form it is preserved at the Great Central along with Post Office Sorting Van 70294. 70294 closely resembles Passenger Brake Vans of the time although it is flat ended without the familiar sloping ends to the roof. It is fitted with TPO collection and delivery equipment which has been fully restored in order that live demonstrations can be made. The interior consists of the usual sorting racks, cooking equipment and lavatory.

Also surviving from the Gresley era are two four-wheeled Passenger Full Brakes. Both 70240 at the North Norfolk Railway and 70250 at the Llangollen Railway have seen the attention of restorers although neither now sees regular use. In addition the underframes of two Parcels & Miscellaneous Vans survive having seen use as Crane Runners with the body work having been removed when converted for this purpose.

5.0.2.2. Thompson Stock

Unlike Gresley stock, Thompson coaches had steel body panels, but for continuity were painted in an imitation teak livery. The exception were certain "tourist stock" vehicles which were painted green and cream.

Post war Thompson design carriages are rather few in preservation. Two of the four corridor carriages came straight from service. Corridor Composite 18477 at the North Yorkshire Moors Railway is now stored awaiting full restoration having seen passenger use when first preserved. Open Third 13803 continues to see occasional use on the Bo.nees and Kinneill Railway. The other two both saw departmental service and are now stored awaiting restoration. Corridor Third 1623 was latterly used as a Civil Engineers Staff Coach and is currently in the early stages of restoration at the North Yorkshire Moors Railway. Corridor Brake Third 1866 saw departmental service as a staff & tool coach, subsequently it has had quite an interesting preservation history. It was initially used as the mainline support coach for locomotive 60532 'BLUE PETER', a function normally fulfilled by British Rail Standard Stock. It followed 'Blue Peter" around its various homes during the 1970s and 1980s eventually ending up at ICI Wilton works. By this time its condition had deteriorated and it was considered no longer suitable for use as a support coach, it thus passed to the Llangollen Railway were it is intended to restore it to its former glory.

The only Thompson catering carriage to survive is Buffet Car 1706. This was one of a pair built for the 'Flying Scotsman' service as Restaurant Buffet Lounge cars. These carriages ran on these prestigious workings from 1948 until 1957. In 1959 they were rebuilt as Restaurant Buffets and continued in service until 1979. Both then were taken into departmental service as Civil Engineers Staff coaches. Regrettably 1705 was scrapped as late as 1989, however 1706 survived and is now undergoing a full restoration before entering service on the Llangollen railway. The two non-corridor carriages preserved have been more fortunate both coming directly from service. Lavatory Composite 88339 has seen many years intermittent use on the North Yorkshire Moors Railway although currently out of service. Brake Composite 80417 has seen many years use since being preserved, including main line service, it can occasionally be savoured today at the Bo'ness & Kinneil Railway.

Four of the Thompson Passenger Brake Vans survive in preservation. As already mentioned two of these 70592 and 70630 saw use in a Safety Exhibition Train although regrettably 70592 has had its bodywork removed, both currently being located at Steamtown Carnforth. These two along with 70621 used for storage purposes on the North Norfolk Railway feature the distinctive deal planking. The only preserved example of the more standard post war design of Passenger Brake Van is 110 which was numbered in the East Coast series. This van currently acts as a workshop/store for carriage restorers on the North Yorkshire Moors Railway awaiting the day when it too receives their attention.

The Chief Engineer's Saloon 900580 and General Managers Saloon 902260 operated as saloons on both the LNER and British Rail until the early 1980s. At this time a realisation of the potential of operating observation saloons on the scenic Scottish lines saw these two saloons taken into capital stock as 1999 and 1998 respectively in the East Coast Joint Stock series. Both saw use on the West Highland extension, 1999 entered service in 1980 and 1998 in 1983. In 1984 both were withdrawn and sold to Flying Scotsman Services at Carnforth. In the late 1980s both were disposed of by Flying Scotsman services. 1998 remains at Carnforth were it is regularly used on the shuttle service. 1999 passed to the Great Scottish & Western Railway Company for use in the 'Royal Scotsman' train for which it was extensively up graded.

A most distinctive vehicle of Thompson design appeared in early British Railways Days. This was the six wheeled Passenger Full Brake. Unlike the similar LMS vehicles these were non-gangwayed. Eighty were constructed and several remained in service until the late 1970s by which time they had been relegated to general parcels traffic. Only two now survive complete in preservation with two bodies and two sets of frames also surviving. It is intended that ancient passenger carrying bodies will be one day mounted on the underframes.

It will be noted that the exact identity of one of the underframes is not known to the authors and obviously any help in establishing the identity of this item would be gratefully appreciated, its present owners seemingly unresponsive to requests for help. Readers wishing to see this underframe are advised that at the time of going to press reports were being received that it may have now left the Penarth Flats storage site. Other storage sites area at Alexandra Dock Junction, Cardiff and Broad Street Bus Garage, Barry and it is possible that it may be now located at one of these.

5.0.3. NON-PASSENGER-CARRYING STOCK

Finally mention should be made of the few vehicles preserved from the non-passenger carrying coaching stock series. The most distinctive of these is General Utility Van 1370, one of only twelve built. This now resides at the Conwy Valley Railway Museum along with several other interesting items of non-passenger carrying coaching stock. Five examples of the four wheeled Covered Carriage Truck survive complete, all but one being from the later batch built in British Railways days. The underframe on the West Somerset Railway has been converted to a flat wagon. This originally arrived on the railway as a complete CCT. Apparently the body suffered some damage and was, in about 1976, removed from the underframe with the help of GWR Pannier Tank 6412, before being used for firewood. Unfortunately, although great effort has been made, it has not been possible to establish the numerical indentity of this vehicle although it is understood to have latterly been internal user 064089. Obviously any help readers can give in ansering this query would be gratefully appreciated. The other complete survivor is a Horse Box which also dates from British Railways days.

5.1. LNER PASSENGER STOCK

5.1.1. EAST COAST JOINT STOCK SERIES

PASSENGER BRAKE, GANGWAYED BG

Order No.: 1180 **Built:** 1948 **Builder:** York **Design:** Thompson
Diagram: 344 **Dimensions:** 63'0'' x 9'0''

110 North Yorkshire Moors Railway

FIRST CLASS SLEEPING CAR SLF

Order No.: 601 **Built:** 1935 **Builder:** Doncaster **Design:** Gresley
Diagram: 157 **Berths:** 10 **Dimensions:** 66'6'' x 9'0''

1211 Strathspey Railway SR No.178

THIRD CLASS SLEEPING CAR (convertible) SLT(C)

Order No.: 356 **Built:** 1930 **Builder:** York **Design:** Gresley
Diagram: 109 **Seats:** 56T or 28 berths **Dimensions:** 61'6'' x 9'0''

1299 DE320931 North Yorkshire Moors Railway

FIRST CLASS SLEEPING CAR SLF

Order No.: 670 **Built:** 1936 **Builder:** Doncaster **Design:** Gresley
Diagram: 157 **Berths:** 10 **Dimensions:** 66'6'' x 9'0''

1591 National Railroad Museum, Green Bay, WI, USA Exported 1969
1592 National Railroad Museum, Green Bay, WI, USA Exported 1969

CORRIDOR THIRD TK

Order No.: 1282 **Built:** 1950 **Builder:** York **Design:** Thompson
Diagram: 329 **Seats:** 42T **Dimensions:** 63'0'' x 9'0''

1623 DE321133 North Yorkshire Moors Railway

RESTAURANT LOUNGE BUFFET (with Kitchen) RLB

Order No.: 1197 **Built:** 1948 **Builder:** Doncaster **Design:** Thompson
Diagram: 352 **Seats:** 8 **Dimensions:** 63'0'' x 9'0''

Converted to Restaurant Buffet (with Kitchen) by British Rail in 1959. Seats 24.

1706 DB975882 Llangollen Railway

CORONATION OBSERVATION SALOON

Order No.: 809 **Built:** 1937 **Builder:** Doncaster **Design:** Gresley
Diagram: 232 **Seats:** 16 **Dimensions:** 51'9'' x 8'10¾''

1719 Great Central Railway
1729 Steamtown Railway Centre, Carnforth

RESTAURANT LOUNGE BUFFET (with Pantry) RLB

Order No.: 842 **Built:** 1938 **Builder:** Doncaster **Design:** Gresley
Diagram: 258 **Seats:** 20F + 5F* **Dimensions:** 61'6'' x 9'0''

* Two seats and a 3-seater setee in Ladies retiring room.
Converted to Restaurant Buffet (with Kitchen) by British Railways. Seats 24U.

1852 Great Central Railway

CORRIDOR BRAKE THIRD BTK

Order No.: 1288 **Built**: 1950 **Builder**: Doncaster **Design**: Thompson
Diagram: 346 **Seats**: 24T **Dimensions**: 63'0'' x 9'0''

1866 DE321120 Llangollen Railway

CHIEF ENGINEERS SALOON

Order No.: **Built**: 1936 **Builder**: Doncaster **Design**: Gresley
Diagram: **Dimensions**: 60'1½'' x 9'0''

900580 DE900580 1998 Steamtown Railway Centre, Carnforth 'LOCH EIL'

GENERAL MANAGERS SALOON

Order No.: **Built**: 1945 **Builder**: York **Design**: Thompson
Diagram: **Dimensions**: 61'6'' x 9'0''

902260 DE902260 1999 Great Scottish & Western Railway Company 'LOCHABER' GSWR99131

5.1.2. GANGWAYED PASSENGER STOCK

These carriages are listed under their 1943 number with any previous numbers carried being listed in the previous column.

OPEN THIRD TO

Order No.: **Built**: 1924 **Builder**: York **Design**: Gresley
Diagram: NE155 **Seats**: 42T **Dimensions**: 53'6'' x 9'0''

North Eastern Railway order.

945 2945 2945 DE320716 North Yorkshire Moors Railway

RESTAURANT FIRST (with Kitchen) RF

Order No.: 59 **Built**: 1925 **Builder**: Stratford **Design**: Gresley
Diagram: 10A **Seats**: 18F **Dimensions**: 61'6'' x 9'0''

676 2865 9002 ADE320921 Battlefield Steam Railway

Order No.: 260 **Built**: 1929 **Builder**: Doncaster **Design**: Gresley
Diagram: 10C **Seats**: 18F **Dimensions**: 61'6'' x 9'0''

42969 9007 ADE320947 North Woolwich Old Station Museum
1222 651 9019 DE320907 Great Central Railway

RESTAURANT THIRD (with Pantry) RT

Order No.: 198 **Built**: 1928 **Builder**: York **Design**: Gresley
Diagram: 112 **Seats**: 39T **Dimensions**: 61'6'' x 9'0''

42972 9066 TDE320927 Mangapp's Farm Railway Museum

RESTAURANT BUFFET (with Kitchen) RB

Order No.: 702 **Built**: 1936 **Builder**: York **Design**: Gresley
Diagram: 167 **Seats**: 24U **Dimensions**: 61'6'' x 9'0''

24079 9115 Mangapp's Farm Railway Museum
24080 9116 TDE321069 096055 Great Central Railway
24082 9118 East Anglian Railway Museum

Order No.: 761 **Built**: 1937 **Builder**: York **Design**: Gresley
Diagram: 167 **Seats**: 24U **Dimensions**: 61'6'' x 9'0''

24278 9122 Great Central Railway
24279 9123 Birmingham Railway Museum

24280	9124	Great Central Railway
51769	9128	North Norfolk Railway
641	9129	North Yorkshire Moors Railway
643	9131	Severn Valley Railway
644	9132	Bo'ness & Kinneil Railway
649	9134	North Yorkshire Moors Railway
650	9135	National Railway Museum

RESTAURANT COMPOSITE (with Kitchen) RC

Order No.: 673 **Built:** 1936 **Builder:** Doncaster **Design:** Gresley
Diagram: 187 **Seats:** 12F 18T **Dimensions:** 61'6" x 9'0"

7960 9162 DE321021 Severn Valley Railway

RESTAURANT BUFFET (with Kitchen) RB

Order No.: 784 **Built:** 1939 **Builder:** Dukinfield **Design:** Gresley
Diagram: 275 **Seats:** 30U **Dimensions:** 61'6" x 9'0"

24287 9195 Steamtown Railway Centre, Carnforth

CORRIDOR BRAKE COMPOSITE BCK

Order No.: 48 **Built:** 1924 **Builder:** York **Design:** Gresley
Diagram: 34 **Seats:** 12F 16T (later 12F 12T) **Dimensions:** 61'6" x 9'0"

10178 1077 52181 10021 ADE320427 041469 North Yorkshire Moors Railway

Order No.: 700 **Built:** 1937 **Builder:** York **Design:** Gresley
Diagram: 175 **Seats:** 12F 24T **Dimensions:** 61'6" x 9'0"

24068 10078 Severn Valley Railway

CORRIDOR BRAKE FIRST BFK

Order No.: 191 **Built:** 1928 **Builder:** York **Design:** Gresley
Diagram: 136 **Seats:** 18F **Dimensions:** 61'6" x 9'0"

4163 11047 ADE320797 Stephenson Railway Museum

CORRIDOR THIRD TK

Order No.: 47 **Built:** 1924 **Builder:** York **Design:** Gresley
Diagram: 23 **Seats:** 64T (later 48T) **Dimensions:** 61'6" x 9'0"

10023 1008 4464 12041 DE320874 Bo'ness & Kinneil Railway

Order No.: 57 **Built:** 1925 **Builder:** York **Design:** Gresley
Diagram: 23 **Seats:** 64T (later 48T) **Dimensions:** 61'6" x 9'0"

1052 4474 12048 DE320744 National Ambulance Museum

THIRD CLASS DINING CAR RTO

Order No.: 382 **Built:** 1931 **Builder:** Doncaster **Design:** Gresley
Diagram: 27A **Seats:** 48T **Dimensions:** 61'6" x 9'0"

6118 12190 DE320897 Llangollen Railway underframe only remains

CORRIDOR THIRD TK

Order No.: **Built:** 1935 **Builder:** BRCW **Design:** Gresley
Diagram: 115 **Seats:** 64T (later 48T) **Dimensions:** 61'6" x 9'0"

23890 12322 TDE320959 North Yorkshire Moors Railway
23896 12328 TDE321008 Steamtown Railway Centre, Carnforth

Order No.: **Built:** 1931 **Builder:** Metro **Design:** Gresley
Diagram: 115 **Seats:** 64T (later 48T) **Dimensions:** 61'6" x 9'0"

3374 12466 DE320894 Bere Ferrers Station Museum, Devon

3291 12481 TDE321007 North Yorkshire Moors Railway
3395 12493 DE320877 North Norfolk Railway

Order No.: 508 **Built**: 1934 **Builder**: York **Design**: Gresley
Diagram: 115 **Seats**: 64T (later 48T) **Dimensions**: 61'6" x 9'0"

1459 12735 DE320966 Bere Ferrers Station Museum, Devon

Order No.: 488 **Built**: 1934 **Builder**: York **Design**: Gresley
Diagram: 155 **Seats**: 42T **Dimensions**: 61'6" x 9'0"

3188 12934 Buckinghamshire Railway Centre

OPEN THIRD TO

* Built with bucket seats.

Order No.: **Built**: 1936 **Builder**: BRCW **Design**: Gresley
Diagram: 186 **Seats**: 64T **Dimensions**: 61'6" x 9'0"

23953 13251 East Anglian Railway Museum
23956 13254 North Yorkshire Moors Railway National Collection
23981* 13279 TDE321070 096056 Great Central Railway

Order No.: **Built**: 1936 **Builder**: Metro **Design**: Gresley
Diagram: 186 **Seats**: 64T **Dimensions**: 61'6" x 9'0"

24105 13317 TDE320957 Severn Valley Railway
24109* 13320 TDE320956 North Yorkshire Moors Railway

Order No.: 559 **Built**: 1934 – 35 **Builder**: York **Design**: Gresley
Diagram: 186 **Seats**: 64T **Dimensions**: 61'6" x 9'0"

43600 13354 TDE320960 Severn Valley Railway
43612 13366 042197 Severn Valley Railway
43632 13385 TDE321006 Embsay Steam Railway
43654 13407 TDE321001 Embsay Steam Railway

Order No.: 594 **Built**: 1935 **Builder**: York **Design**: Gresley
Diagram: 186 **Seats**: 64T **Dimensions**: 61'6" x 9'0"

52255 13547 TDE321005 Severn Valley Railway
52256 13548 TDE321002 Embsay Steam Railway

Order No.: **Built**: 1938 **Builder**: Metro **Design**: Gresley
Diagram: 186 **Seats**: 64T **Dimensions**: 61'6" x 9'0"

56856 13577 TDE321108 North Yorkshire Moors Railway

Order No.: 1126 **Built**: 1947 **Builder**: York **Design**: Thompson
Diagram: 330 **Seats**: 64T **Dimensions**: 63'0" x 9'0"

13803 Bo'ness & Kinneil Railway

CORRIDOR BRAKE THIRD BTK

Order No.: 837 **Built**: 1938 **Builder**: Doncaster **Design**: Gresley
Diagram: 37A **Seats**: 40T (later 30T) **Dimensions**: 61'6" x 9'0"

41384 16076 DE321058 Buckinghamshire Railway Centre

Order No.: 59 **Built**: 1924 **Builder**: Stratford **Design**: Gresley
Diagram: 38 **Seats**: 32T (later 24T) **Dimensions**: 61'6" x 9'0"

62515 4930 16122 ADE320680 Bo'ness & Kinneil Railway

Order No.: **Built**: 1930 **Builder**: BRCW **Design**: Gresley
Diagram: 114 **Seats**: 32T (later 24T) **Dimensions**: 61'6" x 9'0"

3669 16335 ADE320984 Embsay Steam Railway

Order No.: 953 **Built**: 1940 **Builder**: York **Design**: Gresley
Diagram: 178 **Seats**: 36T **Dimensions**: 61'6" x 9'0"

57451 16520 Great Central Railway

OPEN BRAKE THIRD — BTO

Order No.: 565 **Built**: 1935 **Builder**: York **Design**: Gresley
Diagram: 191 **Seats**: 32T **Dimensions**: 61′6″ x 9′0″

43567	16547	North Yorkshire Moors Railway
43571	16551 DE320995 88001	Colne Valley Railway

Order No.: **Built**: 1938 **Builder**: Cravens **Design**: Gresley
Diagram: 196 **Seats**: 48T **Dimensions**: 61′6″ x 9′0″

43556	16631	East Anglian Railway Museum

CORRIDOR COMPOSITE — CK

Order No.: 45 **Built**: 1924 **Builder**: York **Design**: Gresley
Diagram: 7 **Seats**: 15F 40T (later 15F 30T) **Dimensions**: 61′6″ x 9′0″

1065 7781	18033 DE320741	Great Central Railway

Order No.: 1280 **Built**: 1950 **Builder**: York **Design**: Thompson
Diagram: 328 **Seats**: 18F 18T **Dimensions**: 59′6″ x 9′0″

	18477	North Yorkshire Moors Railway

OPEN THIRD — TO

Order No.: 639 **Built**: 1936 **Builder**: York **Design**: Gresley
Diagram: 216 **Seats**: 52T **Dimensions**: 52′6″ x 9′0″

60505	60505 DE321048	Steamtown, Carnforth

Order No.: 661 **Built**: 1936 **Builder**: York **Design**: Gresley
Diagram: 216 **Seats**: 52T **Dimensions**: 52′6″ x 9′0″

60525	60525 DE321049	Steamtown, Carnforth (for NYMR)

CORRIDOR THIRD — TK

Order No.: 107 **Built**: 1926 **Builder**: Stratford **Design**: Gresley
Diagram: 25 **Seats**: 56T **Dimensions**: 52′6″ x 9′0″

61634	61634 DE320904	Nene Valley Railway

CORRIDOR BRAKE THIRD — BTK

Order No.: 146 **Built**: 1927 **Builder**: York **Design**: Gresley
Diagram: 41 **Seats**: 24T **Dimensions**: 52′6″ x 9′0″

62565	62565 DE320746	Great Central Railway

5.1.3. PASSENGER FULL BRAKES & VANS

These carriages are listed under their 1943 number with any previous numbers carried being listed in the previous column.

PARCELS & MISCELLANEOUS VAN — PMV

Four-wheeled.

Order No.: 125 **Built**: 1926–27 **Builder**: Stratford
Diagram: 86 **Dimensions**: 32′0″ x 8′10″

6259	70107 DE320952	National Railway Museum	Reduced to Crane Runner
6282	70130 DE321051	Stephenson Railway Museum	Reduced to Crane Runner

PASSENGER BRAKE, NON–GANGWAYED — BY

Four-wheeled.

Order No.: 325 **Built**: 1929–30 **Builder**: York
Diagram: 120 **Dimensions**: 32′0″ x 9′0″

772	70240 040923	North Norfolk Railway
6854 776	70250	Llangollen Railway

PASSENGER BRAKE, GANGWAYED — BGP

With shelves for pigeon traffic.

Order No.: 400 **Built**: 1931 **Builder**: Doncaster **Design**: Gresley
Diagram: 129 **Dimensions**: 51′1½″ x 9′0″

6777	70268	Great Central Railway

POST OFFICE SORTING VAN — POS

Order No.: 787 **Built**: 1937 **Builder**: York **Design**: Gresley
Diagram: 164 **Dimensions**: 60′1½″ x 9′0″

2441	70294	Great Central Railway

PASSENGER BRAKE, GANGWAYED — BGP

With shelves for pigeon traffic.

Order No.: 656 **Built**: 1936 **Builder**: York **Design**: Gresley
Diagram: 198 **Dimensions**: 61′6″ x 9′0″

4149	70361	Lakeside Railway

Order No.: 1017 **Built**: 1941 **Builder**: York **Design**: Gresley
Diagram: 245 **Dimensions**: 61′6″ x 9′0″

4050	70427	Great Central Railway
4069	70442	East Anglian Railway Museum

Order No.: 777 **Built**: 1938 **Builder**: York **Design**: Gresley
Diagram: 245 **Dimensions**: 61′6″ x 9′0″

4237	70460	ADB975242	Steamtown Railway Centre, Carnforth	Body only remains
4247	70470		Keighley & Worth Valley Railway	K&WVR No.106

Order No.: 983 **Built**: 1940 **Builder**: York **Design**: Gresley
Diagram: 245 **Dimensions**: 61′6″ x 9′0″

4268	70491	MM3023	99628	ZDB975399	Llangollen Railway
4271	70494				Bo'ness & Kinneil Railway

PASSENGER BRAKE, GANGWAYED — BG

Order No.: 1123 **Built**: 1945–46 **Builder**: York **Design**: Thompson
Diagram: 327 **Dimensions**: 61′6″ x 9′0″

70592	MM3021	99626	ZDB975400	Steamtown Railway Centre, Carnforth — underframe only remains
70621				North Norfolk Railway
70630	MM3022	99627	ZDB975401	Steamtown Railway Centre, Carnforth

PASSENGER BRAKE, NON-GANGWAYED — BZ

Six-wheeled.

Order No.: 1284 **Built**: 1950 **Builder**: Stratford **Design**: Thompson
Diagram: 358 **Dimensions**: 32′0″ x 9′0″

70653	Great Central Railway	Body only remains at Loughborough
70654	Great Central Railway	
70668	Great Central Railway	Body only remains at Rothley
70687	North Yorkshire Moors Railway	
70692	Mangapp's Farm Railway Museum	underframe only remains
70XXX	National Museum of Wales, Penarth Store	underframe only remains

PASSENGER BRAKE, GANGWAYED — BG

Order No.: 1059 **Built**: 1943 **Builder**: York **Design**: Gresley
Diagram: 260 **Dimensions**: 61′6″ x 9′0″

957	70741	Venice-Simplon Orient Express	'BAGGAGE CAR NO.7'

PASSENGER BRAKE, GANGWAYED — BGP

With shelves for pigeon traffic.

Order No.: 1073 **Built:** 1943 **Builder:** York **Design:** Gresley
Diagram: 245 **Dimensions:** 61'6" x 9'0"

70754 041366	Stephenson Railway Museum
70759	South Devon Railway

5.1.4. NON-GANGWAYED PASSENGER STOCK

These carriages are listed under their 1943 number with any previous numbers carried being listed in the previous column.

COMPOSITE BRAKE — BC

Order No.: **Built:** 1952 **Builder:** BRCW **Design:** Thompson
Diagram: 360 **Seats:** 16F 40T **Dimensions:** 52'4" x 9'0"

80417 — Bo'ness & Kinneil Railway

FIRST — F

Order No.: 148 **Built:** 1927 **Builder:** York **Design:** Gresley
Diagram: 48 **Seats:** 56F **Dimensions:** 51'1½" x 9'0"

Declassified to third (seats 70T).

6449	81052 ADE320889 041568	Holme Trading Estate	underframe only remains

THIRD — T

Order No.: **Built:** 1926 **Builder:** Metro **Design:** Gresley
Diagram: 56 **Seats:** 80T **Dimensions:** 51'1½" x 9'0"

22219 61857	82145 DE320832	Buckinghamshire Railway Centre

Order No.: **Built:** 1927 **Builder:** Cravens **Design:** Gresley
Diagram: 57 **Seats:** 80T **Dimensions:** 51'1½" x 9'0"

61684	82347 DE320803	Mangapp's Farm Railway Museum

BRAKE THIRD — BT

Order No.: **Built:** 1926 **Builder:** Clayton **Design:** Gresley
Diagram: 64 **Seats:** 40T **Dimensions:** 51'1½" x 9'0"

3641	86056 KDE320779	Mangapp's Farm Railway Museum

Order No.: 207 **Built:** 1927 **Builder:** York **Design:** Gresley
Diagram: 65 **Seats:** 40T **Dimensions:** 51'1½" x 9'0"

22313	86062 DE320882	Nene Valley Railway	Reduced to Crane Runner

Order No.: 149 **Built:** 1926 **Builder:** York **Design:** Gresley
Diagram: 65 **Seats:** 40T **Dimensions:** 51'1½" x 9'0"

3107	86072 KDE320759	Bere Ferrers Station Museum, Devon

ARTICULATED SUBURBAN QUADRUPLETS — QUAD-ART

Order No.: **Built:** 1924 **Builder:** Doncaster **Design:** Gresley
Diagram: GN478 **Dimensions:** 38'1¼" x 9'0" (8941/2) 43'6" x 9'0" (8943/4).

Quad-art set 74. 8943/4 were originally composites seating 40F 36T.

8941	48941	86272	86762	Brake third	Dia. 68B	Seats: 60T	North Norfolk Railway
8942	48942	86273	86763	Third	Dia. 69	Seats: 84T	North Norfolk Railway
8943	48943	86274	86764	Third	Dia. 70	Seats: 84T	North Norfolk Railway
8944	48944	86275	86765	Third	Dia. 71	Seats: 84T	North Norfolk Railway

COMPOSITE with LAVATORY CL

Order No.: 327 **Built:** 1930 **Builder:** Dukinfield **Design:** Gresley
Diagram: 50 **Seats:** 19F 33T **Dimensions:** 51'1½" x 9'0"

32455	88026 DE321015	Derwent Valley Light Railway

Order No.: **Built:** 1947 **Builder:** Cravens **Design:** Thompson
Diagram: 338 **Seats:** 19F 33T **Dimensions:** 52'4" x 9'0"

	88339	North Yorkshire Moors Railway

5.2. LNER NPCCS

COVERED CARRIAGE TRUCK CCT

4-wheel

Diagram: 6 **Built:** 1939 **Builder:** York

1298		Monkwearmouth Station Museum	
12XX	064089	West Somerset Railway	underframe only remains

Diagram: 6 **Built:** 1950 **Builder:** York

1308	041344	North Yorkshire Moors Railway	
1322	RDB975792	North Yorkshire Moors Railway	
1334		Keighley & Worth Valley Railway	K&WVR No.108
1345		Southall Railway Centre	

GENERAL UTILITY VAN GUV

Diagram: 7 **Built:** 1950 **Builder:** York

1370 Conwy Valley Railway Museum

HORSE BOX HB

4-wheel

Diagram: 9 **Built:** 1954 **Builder:** Earlestown

2459 Steamport Railway Museum

6. WAGONS-LITS NIGHT FERRY STOCK

Twenty-five steel bodied sleeping cars, known as Type F (for Ferry) were built for the 'Night Ferry', a train running between London Victoria and Dover with the Sleeping Cars being conveyed onward to European destinations. Those interested in further information regarding this train are referred to:-

Night Ferry/George Behrend and Gary Buchanan – St. Martin: Jersey Artists Ltd. 1985.

All twenty five cars were identical in layout, with nine compartments each containing an upper and a lower berth, the upper berth being folded back out of use when the compartment was used for single occupancy. Heating was by a coke stove. Two of these are now preserved in Great Britain. 3792 was one of the original cars being built in 2936 by ANF Blanc-Misseron. It was withdrawn in 1974 and restored by Wagons-Lits at their Oostende works in 1978 – 79. It was officially handed to the National Railway Museum on 16th January 1980 and has been on almost constant display since. 3801 was built in 1939 by CGC St. Denis and was used in the formation of the last Paris – London 'Night Ferry' on the night of 31st October/1st November 1980. following several years storage at Oostende this car moved to the Bluebell Railway in December 1984.

CONVERTIBLE SLEEPING CAR SLE

Built: 1936 **Builder:** ANF Blanc-Misseron **Berths:** 18

3792 National Railway Museum

Built: 1939 **Builder:** CGC St. Denis **Berths:** 18

3801 Bluebell Railway

7. BODIES OF NON PASSENGER CARRYING COACHING STOCK

Throughout the main body of this book details have been given of items at preservation and similar sites which have had the underframe and running gear removed and thus only a body remains. Normally these see use as store sheds or similar. In addition several scrap merchants have sold on the bodies of items being scrapped in particular to farmers and industrialists. It is normally only by chance that these are discovered by enthusiasts and those known to the authors are listed below along with their current locations. Few details are given about these bodies other than company design, type and numbers carried. Those requiring further detail are referred to the introductory paragraphs to the various sections of this book were recommended books giving such information are listed.

In the following listing it will be noted that two basic designs predominate. These being the GWR design Fruit D and the Southern Railway PMV/CCT both of which have had a reputation for robust construction emphasised by the fact that several of those listed have moved several times in private ownership. A total of one hundred and seventy Fruit Ds were built to the GWR design with a further one hundred and fifteen following to British Rail lots. It has not been possible to identify several of the Fruit D bodies discovered and these are listed here although it is possible that these particular examples are built to BR lots and should be included in the similar listing in the first book of this series. It will also be noted that many of the Fruit D bodies are located in Warwickshire and surrounding counties and it is anticipated that several others remain as yet undiscovered in these areas.

Obviously the author would be very interested to here of further bodies which exist in order that details can be included in future editions of this book.

It is also worth adding that a number of non passenger carrying bodies are retained by British Rail at various locations on the Railtrack network. Regular up dates are given regarding these in the ''Departmental Stock'' section of the ''The Railway Observer'', the monthly magazine of The Railway Correspondence and Travel Society.

Co.	*Type*	*Numbers*	*Use*	*Location*	*Grid Reference*
GWR	ROYAL SALOON	283, 8283	Bowling Alley	Opposite the entrance to Youlston Park, Shirwell, Barnstaple, Devon	SS 592374
GWR	HORSE BOX	?	Potting Shed	Allotments, Carmarthen, Dyfed	SN 403199
GWR	FRUIT D	2298, DB975343	Store Shed	James & Crook (Dean Woodstoves), Unit 48, Lydney Industrial Estate, Lydney, Gloucestershire	SO 645018
GWR	FRUIT D	2339	Store Shed	Manor Farm, Illmington, Warwickshire	SP 216441
GWR	FRUIT D	2349	Cattle or Store Shed	Manor Farm, Illmington, Warwickshire	SP214443 or SP 216441
GWR	SIPHON G	2992	Staff Room	Spa-Tec, Buxworth Basin, Buxworth, Derbyshire	SK 018822
GWR	FRUIT D	3410	Store Shed	Manor Farm, Lower Arncott, Bicester	SP 607182
GWR	FRUIT D	3413	Cattle or Store Shed	Manor Farm, Illmington, Warwickshire	SP 214443 or SP 216441
GWR	FRUIT D	3414	Store Shed	Blackwell Court Scouting Centre, Blackwell Court, Bromsgrove, Worcestershire	SP 993716
GWR	FRUIT D	3415, DB975333	Store Shed	Havenplan, Station Road, Killamarsh, Derbyshire	SK 449809
GWR	FRUIT D	3446,DB975176	Store Shed	Farm, Nupton-on-the-Hill, Warwickshire	SP 454613
GWR	FRUIT D	3453	Store Shed	Birds Commercial Metals, Long Marston, Worcestershire	SP 154458
GWR	FRUIT D	3470	Cattle or Store Shed	Manor Farm, Illmington, Warwickshire	SP 214443 or SP216441

GWR	FRUIT D	3476	Pig Sty	Ashtree Lodge, Chipping Warden, near Banbury, Northamptonshire	SP 484498
GWR	FRUIT D	3478, DB975338	Aviary	Cocomar, Bevercotes Road, Tuxford, Nottinghamshire	SY 734714
GWR	FRUIT D	3479	Store Shed	Spetchley Fruit Farm, Low Hill, White Ladies Aston, Worcestershire	SP 913518
GWR	FRUIT D	3480	Pig Sty	Field, Illmington, Warwickshire	SP 218439
GWR/BR?	FRUIT D	?	Pig Sty	Ashtree Lodge, Chipping Warden, near Banbury, Northamptonshire	SP 484498
GWR/BR?	FRUIT D	?	Derelict Store	Spetchley Fruit Farm, Low Hill, White Ladies Aston, Worcestershire	SP 914518
GWR/BR?	FRUIT D	?	Stable	Field, Bubbenhall Bridge, Bubbenhall, Warwickshire	SP 354726
SR	PMV	1053	Store Shed	Newport Docks, Newport, Gwent	
SR	PMV	1091	Store Shed	Blackwell Court Scouting Centre, Blackwell Court, Bromsgrove, Worcs.	SP 993716
SR	PMV	1115	Store Shed	Blackwell Court Scouting Centre, Blackwell Court, Bromsgrove, Worcs.	SP 993716
SR	PMV	1123	Store Shed	Stanfree, Clowne, Derbyshire	SK 471735
SR	PMV	1126, 041492	Store Shed	J. Murphy & Sons, Goodman, Street, Leeds, West Yorkshire	
SR	PMV	1264	Store Shed	Car Fragmentation, Ridham Dock, Kent	
SR	CCT	1427	Store Shed	Orchard, Junction of A44/A46, Evesham Bypass, Evesham, Worcestershire	SP 057424
SR	PMV	1479	Store Shed	Field, Wenvoe, Barry, South Glamorgan	ST 124728
SR	PMV	1485	Store Shed	Parks Farm, Evesham, Worcestershire	SP 055448
SR	PMV	1535	Store Shed	Windmill City Farm, Bedminster, Bristol, Avon	ST 58X71X
SR	PMV	1544	Store Shed	Farm, Seavington St. Michael, Ilminster, Somerset	
SR	PMV	1608	Derelict Store	Derelict Factory, Garn-Yr-Erw, Blaenavon, Gwent	SO 229103
SR	CCT	1780	Store Shed	Mill Batch Farm, Perry Road, Mark, near Blackford, Somerset	ST 387478
SR	PMV	2147	Store Shed	Febry Transport Ltd., Greystones, Colt Green, Old Sodbury, Glos.	ST 739817
SR	CCT	2494	Store Shed	Martins Corner, Long Marston, Worcestershire	SP 143482
SR	PMV	?	Store Shed	Temple Normanton Business Park, Chesterfield, Derbyshire	SK 413677
SR	PMV	?	Store Shed	Poppleton Road Allotments, Poppleton Road, York, North, Yorkshire	SE 579525
LMS	MCV	35583	Store Shed	Blackwell Court Scouting Centre, Blackwell Court, Bromsgrove, Worcs	SP 993716
LMS	MCV	37013	Stable	Woodall, Harthill, South Yorkshire	SK 481808
LMS	FISH VAN	40228	Store Shed	G.R. Barratt & Sons Ltd, Housleys Scrapyard, Retford Rd, Woodhouse Mill, Sheffield	SK 434857
LMS	FISH VAN	40231	Store Shed	G.R. Barratt & Sons Ltd, Housleys Scrapyard, Retford Rd, Woodhouse Mill, Sheffield	SK 434857
LMS	FISH VAN	40258	Store Shed	C.C. Crump Wagon Repair Works, Connahs Quay, Shotton, Clwyd	SJ 296697
LMS	FISH VAN	?	Store Shed	Haven Plan, Station Road, Killamarsh, Derbyshire	SK 449809
LNER	CCT	1349	Stable	Marston Grange, Long Marston, Worcestershire	SP 154458

APPENDIX 1

PRIVATELY OWNED MAINLINE POST-GROUPING CARRIAGES

It may surprise readers how many of the carriages included in this book have been passed for mainline use since the 'plated' system was introduced in January 1974. In the following, details are given of those once 'plated' but no longer passed, those currently plated being detailed in the main body of the book.

H.P. BULMER LTD. 'THE BULMERS CIDER PULLMAN TRAIN'

This train heralded the return of mainline steam in the early 1970s and was formed:-

BLM99200	305 AQUILLA	Pullman Kitchen First	
BLM99201	219 CAR No. 64	Pullman Parlour Third	'CHRISTINE'
BLM99202	229 CAR No. 76	Pullman Parlour Third	'EVE'
BLM99203	261 CAR No. 83	Pullman Parlour Third	'PRINIA'
BLM99204	194 CAR No. 36	Pullman Brake Third	'MORELLA'
BLM99205	15829	BR Mark I Corridor Composite	

It was not intended to be a mainline set as such, more a mobile exhibition/hospitality train for the Bulmers company. Three of the Pullman Cars were converted internally for exhibition purposes as a museum, a cinema, and a bar, and four of them had been named after Director's wives. 'MORELLA', originally Pullman Car No 36 was the cinema, and was named after the wife of Mr Esmond Bulmer; EVE, originally Car No 76 was the bar product display coach and named after Mrs Brian Nelson; PRINIA, originally Car No 83 was named after the wife of Mr Peter Prior and was the museum car displaying the development of H.P. Bulmer; and 'CHRISTINE', originally Car No 64 was retained in its original form as a dining car, and was named after Mrs Bertram Bulmer. The fifth car AQUILLA, with its original name retained was kept in virtually original condition except for the fitting of a new kitchen range and new carpeting. Following several succesful tours when it was headed by such prestigious locomotives as 'Flying Scotsman' and 'King George V' the set was retired to the H. P. Bulmer headquarters at Hereford. The Pullman cars continued their Exhibition/hospitality function there for many years before being sold to the Venice-Simplon Orient Express in the late 1980s. Car No 83 remain at Stewarts Lane awaiting restoration, however Car No 64 has been restored and is now based at the Bluebell Railway whilst Car No 36 is restored and named 'HERMIONE' at the Colne Valley Railway and Car No. 76 is now stored at the Bluebell Railway awaiting further restoration. The other two carriages are not detailed in this book, being of later design, but are however worthy of mention. Pullman Car 'AQUILLA' now being preserved at the Colne Valley Railway where it sees regular use on the short but interesting line there. Corridor Composite 15829 was transferred to the ownership of Steam in Hereford Ltd at the associated Bulmers Railway Centre were it saw use in their mainline set (see below) and on internal shuttle workings. Following closure of the centre it was moved to the Dean Forest Railway and then to the Gwili Railway.

STEAM IN HEREFORD LTD. MAIN LINE SUPPORT SET

Three carriages were passed for mainline use based at the Bulmers Railway Centre, including the BR Mark I Corridor Composite used initially in the 'Bulmers Cider Pullman Train'. The carriages involved being:-

SHL99850	35219	BR Mark I Corridor Brake Second
SHL99851	15829	BR Mark I Corridor Composite
SHL99852	9115	LNER Restaurant Buffet with Kitchen

This set appears to have been used for mainline support duties and similar activities. Following the closure of the Bulmers Railway Centre the LNER Restaurant Buffet was moved to the Llangollen Railway were it saw regular use as a Buffet Car on trains on this rapidly developing railway. It has however recently moved again and is resident at the delightful Mangapps Farm Railway Museum.

SEVERN VALLEY RAILWAY. 'GREAT WESTERN RAILWAY MAIN LINE SET''

This was one of two sets of Great Western carriages which operated on the mainline during the late 1970s being formed:-

SVR99230	5883	GWR Corridor Brake Third
SVR99231	1116	GWR Corridor Third
SVR99232	1146	GWR Corridor Third

SVR99233	9631	GWR Restaurant Buffet with Kitchen
SVR99234	1086	GWR Corridor Third
SVR99235	1087	GWR Corridor Third
SVR99236	7284	GWR Corridor Composite
SVR99237	9627	GWR Third Class Dining Car
SVR99238	6562	GWR Corridor Brake Composite
SVR99239	2119	GWR Corridor Third
SVR99240	6913	GWR Corridor Brake Composite
CARP99730	9615	GWR Restaurant First with Kitchen

GREAT WESTERN SOCIETY. 'GREAT WESTERN RAILWAY' MAIN LINE SET

This was the other set of Great Western carriages used on the main line:-

GWS99500	1111		GWR Corridor Third
GWS99501	1289		GWR Open Third
GWS99502	7371		GWR Corridor Brake Composite
GWS99503	5952		GWR Corridor Third
GWS99504	536		GWR Corridor Third
GWS99505	7313		GWR Corridor Composite
GWS99506	9112	QUEEN MARY	GWR First Class Super Saloon
GWS99507	9118	PRINCESS ELIZABETH	GWR First Class Super Saloon
GWS99509	7372		GWR Corridor Brake Composite
GWS99510	2202		GWR Corridor Brake Third

DART VALLEY RAILWAY PLC. MAINLINE SET

The Dart Valley Railway did for a period in the 1970s operate a twelve coach mainline set which included two grouping era carriages. The set being:-

DVR99600	3081	BR Mark I Open First (prototype)
DVR99601	3084	BR Mark I Open First (prototype)
DVR99602	4317	BR Mark I Tourist Second Open
DVR99603	4288	BR Mark I Tourist Second Open
DVR99604	4046	BR Mark I Tourist Second Open
DVR99605	4166	BR Mark I Tourist Second Open
DVR99606	4654	BR Mark I Tourist Second Open
DVR99607	4275	BR Mark I Tourist Second Open
DVR99608	4289	BR Mark I Tourist Second Open
DVR99609	4507	BR Mark I Tourist Second Open
DVR99610	9129	LNER Restaurant Buffet with Kitchen
DVR99611	Car No 13	Pullman Observation Saloon

The two grouping carriages both remain. The Pullman Observation Saloon being regularly used on the Dart Valley Railways Paignton & Dartmouth line from which good views are afforded of this scenic line. The LNER Restaurant Buffet was sold to the North Yorkshire Moors Railway in 1983 were an extensive ten year restoration has produced the immaculate vehicle it is today. This set should not be confused with the carriages used in the mid 1980s under the Totnes running powers agreement although the Pullman Observation saloon was involved. The Totnes running agreement allowed trains of Dart Valley Railway locomotives and carriages to run into the British Rail station at Totnes. The carriages used were not passed for main line running, being restricted to 35 mph. Other Grouping carriages involved being GWR Corridor Brake Composite 7377 and GWR Auto Trailer 228.

STRATHSPEY RAILWAY

This railway has had a small fleet of LMS carriages passed for mainline use as follows:-

SPEY99700	33003	LMS Passenger Brake, Gangwayed (6-wheel)
SPEY99701	27043	LMS Brake Corridor Third
SPEY99702	45021	LMS District Engineers Saloon
SPEY99703	27234	LMS Open Third

SCOTTISH RAILWAY PRESERVATION SOCIETY. MAINLINE SET

It may be a surprise to realise that over the years the SRPS has had over thirty carriages passed for mainline use. For many years now those used in the mainline set have been of BR design. The first four passed for mainline use were actually pre-grouping carriages followed by the following grouping carriages:-

SCR99804	24725	LMS Corridor Composite
SCR99805	27407	LMS Open Third

SCR99806	9132	LNER Restaurant Buffet with Kitchen
SCR99807	80417	LNER Brake Composite
SCR99808	27389	LMS Open Third

All these five are now located on the Bo'ness and Kinneil Railway, the majority seeing occasional use on passenger trains.

VENICE-SIMPLON ORIENT EXPRESS

This set which is predominantly formed of Pullman Cars has now been running for over ten years. In that time only one carriage has been stood down this being:-

VSOE99537	70741	LNER Passenger Brake, Gangwayed

This was the original luggage van used when the set was inaugurated in 1984, being branded 'Baggage Car No 7'. Initially its private owner number was VSOE99637, however this was altered in order to avoid a duplicate number on the BR TOPS computer, 99637 being the number of an exhibition van.

GREAT SCOTTISH & WESTERN RAILWAY COMPANY. 'ROYAL SCOTSMAN'

Regrettably one of only two pre-natinalisation carriages formed in this luxuriant set has been stood down, this being:-

GSWR99960	12322	LNER Corridor Third

This was the original dining car formed in the train having been considerably altered from its original internal layout. Regrettably it was involved in a collision in Millerhill Yard. The damage incurred was considered too great to allow it to run again on the mainline thus it was replaced in the set with a further Pullman conversion. The carriage is now located at the North Yorkshire Moors Railway following a period of storage at the premises of Lancastrian Carriage and Wagon. It is understood that it will now be restored for use on trains operating on its host railway.

STEAMTOWN RAILWAY MUSEUM

During the 1970s and 1980s whilst in the ownership of Sir William McAlpine Steamtown Railway Museum had four carriages registered for main line use in its own right as opposed to carriages in Sir William's private train these being:-

STRM99054	9195	LNER Restaurant Buffet
STRM99055	395	LMS First Class Sleeping Car
STRM99064	45005	LMS Chairman's Saloon
STRM99065	900580	LNER Chief Civil Engineer's Saloon

All remain at Carnforth although the LMS Chairman's Saloon is now officially owned by the Carriage & Traction Company, a subsidiary of Flying Scotsman Railways and is expected to move shortly.

STANDARD GAUGE STEAM TRUST, BIRMINGHAM RAILWAY MUSEUM

Three carriages from the grouping era have been plated by the Standard Gauge Steam Trust principally being used as saloons for mainline operations. The carriages involved being:-

SGST99100	255 IONE	Pullman Kitchen First
SGST99103	80972	GWR Inspection Saloon
SGST99106	9001	GWR Special Saloon

The Pullman car is of course now part of the Venice-Simplon Orient Express set and still passed for mainline use although with a different private owner number. The two GWR saloons currently are located on the Great Central Railway were they are used for special workings.

BLUE PETER LOCOMOTIVE SOCIETY. 60532 SUPPORT COACH

The Blue Peter Locomotive Society are unique amongst the operators of steam locomotives on the main line in that they did not use a British Rail design carriage as a support coach. Instead they used Thompson design LNER Corridor Brake Third for the period in the 1970s when locomotive 60532 'BLUE PETER' was in use on the mainline, details being:-

BPLS99400	1866	LNER Corridor Brake Third

Following a number of years storage a ICI Wilton this coach has been moved to the Llangollen Railway were it awaits restoration.

CHELL INSTRUMENTS.

Chell instruments provide the support coach for locomotive 71000 'DUKE OF GLOUCESTER'. in addition they also have had the preserved GWR Dynamometer Car passed for mainline use:-

CHEL99140	796	GWR Corridor Third	(converted to Dynamometer Car)

APPENDIX TWO

MOBILE CONTROL TRAINS

Throughout this book mention has been made of the twelve mobile control trains, many of the carriages included in these now being preserved. Below is given the formation of these trains along with a few other details which may interest readers.

The first column gives the number carried when in use as a mobile control train coach. It should be noted that Scottish Region trains kept their capital stock numbers. The second column gives details of the vehicle type and former capital stock number. The third column gives details of the final allocation and the fourth column gives the present location of the vehicle.

Scottish Region - Two Trains

SC16187E	LNER BTK	Carstairs	Scrapped
SC12934E	LNER TK	Carstairs	Buckinghamshire Railway Centre
SC12937E	LNER TK	Carstairs	Scrapped
SC13251E	LNER TO	Carstairs	East Anglian Railway Museum
SC16198E	LNER BTK	Carstairs	Scrapped
SC12504E	LNER TK	Carstairs	Scrapped
SC13254E	LNER TO	Carstairs	North Yorkshire Moors Railway
SC12936E	LNER TK	Carstairs	Scrapped

Southern Region - TwoTrains

DS70159	SR BTK 3680	Tunbridge Wells West	Departmental use
DS70160	SR BTK 3687	Tunbridge Wells West	Bluebell Railway
DS70161	SR CK 5599	Tunbridge Wells West	Scrapped
DS70162	SR CK 5601	Faversham	Scrapped
DS70163	SR BTK 3690	Faversham	Spa Valley Railway
DS70164	SR BTK 3691	Faversham	Departmental use
DS70165	SE&CR PMV 1996	Tunbridge Wells West	Mangapps Farm
DS70166	SE&CR PMV 2001	Faversham	Scrapped

Western Region - Two Trains

DW150027	GWR Siphon G 2790	Craven Arms	Dean Forest Railway
DW150028	GWR Siphon G 2775	Craven Arms	National Railway Museum
DW150029	GWR TK 5848	Craven Arms	Dean Forest Railway
DW150030	GWR TK 5929	Craven Arms	Dean Forest Railway
DW150031	GWR TK 5856	Craven Arms	Tintern Parva Station
DW150032	GWR RTO 9653	Craven Arms	Severn Valley Railway
DW150323	GWR Siphon G 2798	Craven Arms	Scrapped
DW150324	GWR TK 5813	Craven Arms	Dean Forest Railway
DW150326	GWR RTO 9654	Craven Arms	Severn Valley Railway

Eastern Region - Four trains

DE320953	LNER TO 13273	Heaton	Scrapped
DE320954	LNER TK 12715	Heaton	Scrapped
DE320955	LNER TK 12394	Heaton	Scrapped
DE320956	LNER TO 13320	Heaton	North Yorkshire Moors Railway
DE320957	LNER TO 13317	York	Severn Valley Railway
DE320958	LNER TK 12523	York	Scrapped
DE320959	LNER TK 12322	York	North Yorkshire Moors Railway
DE320960	LNER TO 13354	York	Severn Valley Railway
DE321001	LNER TO 13407	Doncaster	Embsay Steam Railway
DE321002	LNER TO 13548	Doncaster	Embsay Steam Railway
DE321003	LNER TK 12262	Doncaster	Scrapped
DE321004	LNER TK 12726	Doncaster	Scrapped
DE321005	LNER TO 13547	Doncaster	Severn Valley Railway
DE321006	LNER TO 13385	Doncaster	Embsay Steam Railway
DE321007	LNER TK 12481	Doncaster	North Yorkshire Moors Railway
DE321008	LNER TK 12328	Doncaster	Steamtown Railway Centre

London Midland Region - Two trains

DM395342	LMS TK 1213	Springs Branch	Scrapped
DM395343	LMS TK 1234	Springs Branch	Scrapped
DM395344	LMS TO 7820	Springs Branch	Buckinghamshire Railway Centre
DM395345	LMS TO 7828	Springs Branch	National Railway Museum
DM395346	LMS TO 7863	Springs Branch	Midland Railway Centre
DM395347	LMS TO 7868	Springs Branch	Somerset and Avon Railway

APPENDIX THREE

GROUPING COACHES IN THE NATIONAL COLLECTION

Detailed below are the grouping carriages which currently form part of the national collection and their current status and whereabouts.

Pullman Car Company

TOPAZ	Pullman Parlour First	On display outside the Main Hall at York

Great Western Railway

2775	Siphon G	Stored in the South Yard at York
9006	Royal Saloon	Stored at MoD BAD Kineton, Warwickshire
9007	Royal Saloon	On display at Bishops Lydeard, West Somerset Railway
9631	Restaurant Buffet with kitchen	On display in the Main Hall at York
9653	Third Class Dining Car	In use on the Severn Valley Railway
9654	Third Class Dining Car	In use on the Severn Valley Railway
80970	Inspection Saloon	Stored at MoD BAD Kineton, Warwickshire
112884	Mink G	On display in the South Hall at York

Southern Railway

435	Passenger Brake (4-w, Gang'd)	Stored outside the main hall at York
1456	Open Third	Stored at the Bluebell Railway
4920	Postal Office Sorting Van	In use as museum coach at Nene Valley Railway

London Midland & Scottish Railway

798	Royal Saloon	On display at Kelvin Hall, Glasgow
799	Royal Saloon	On display in the South Hall at York
5987	Corridor Brake Third	On display at the Steamtown Railway Centre, Carnforth
7828	Open Third	Stored outside the Main Hall at York
14241	Convertible Sleeping Car	On display in the Main Hall at York
27093	Corridor Brake Third	On display at the Midland Railway Centrei
30272	Post Office Sorting Van	On display at the Nene Valley Railway
44057	Milk Tank	On display in the South Hall at York
45049	Dynamometer Car	Stored at the East Lancashire Railway
45053	Mobile Test Unit	Stored in the South Yard at York

London & North Eastern Railway

9135	Restaurant Buffet with Kitchen	On display in the Locomotive Building at York
13254	Open Third	Stored at the North Yorkshire Moors Railway
70107	Parcels & Miscellaneous Van	On display in the museum garden at York

Wagons Lits

3792	Sleeping Car	On display in the South Hall at York

LIST OF LOCATIONS

The following is a list of UK locations where the carriages included in this book can be found, together with Ordnance Survey grid references where these are known. At certain locations, particularly the larger private railways, carriages may be dispersed at several sites. In such cases the principle site where carriages can normally be found is the one given. Enquiries at this location may reveal the whereabouts of other carriages. Details of carriages stored on a long term basis away from their home location are generally given in the text of this book.

Location/Base	*OS Grid Ref.*
ADtranz, Doncaster Works, Doncaster, South Yorkshire (Private Site)	SE565029
A.E. Knill & Co Ltd, No.1 Dock, Barry, South Glamorgan (Private Site)	ST118676
Avon Valley Railway, Bitton Station, Bristol, Avon	ST670705
Barnwell Junction, Cambridge (Private Site)	TL473598
Battlefield Steam Railway, Shackerstone Station, Shackerstone, Leicestershire	SK379066
Bere Ferrers Station Museum, Bere Ferrers, Devon	SX452635
Bideford Station Museum, Bideford, Devon	SS458264
Birmingham Railway Museum, Tyseley Depot, Tyseley, Birmingham, West Midlands	SP105841
Blackland Railway, Dykes Farm, Blackland, Calne, Wiltshire (Private Site)	SU008687
Bluebell Railway Company, Sheffield Park, Uckfield, East Sussex	TQ403238
Bo'ness & Kinneil Railway, Bo'ness Station, Bo'ness, West Lothian	NT003817
Bodmin Steam Railway, Bodmin General Station, Bodmin, Cornwall	SX073664
Brecon Mountain Railway, Pant Station, Dowlais, Merthyr Tydfil, Mid-Glamorgan	SO063120
Brighton Railway Museum, Preston Park Works, Brighton, East Sussex	TQ302061
British Rail Staff Association, Aylesbury, Buckinghamshire	SP818134
Buckinghamshire Railway Centre, Quainton Road Station, Aylesbury, Buckinghamshire	SP736189
Caerphilly Railway, Harold Wilson Industrial Estate, Caerphilly, Mid-Glamorgan	ST163865
Caledonian Railway, Brechin Station, Brechin, Angus, Tayside	NO603603
Carriage & Traction Company Ltd (Stock stored at various U.K. locations)	
Chasewater Railway, Chasewater Pleasure Park, Brownhills, West Midlands	SK034070
Cheddleton Railway Centre, Cheddleton Station, Cheddleton, Leek, Staffordshire	SJ983519
Chinnor and Princess Risborough Railway, Chinnor Cement Works, Chinnor, Oxon.	SP756004
Cholsey & Wallingford Railway, Hithercroft Industrial Estate, Wallingford, Oxfordshire	SU599891
Colne Valley Railway, Castle Hedingham Station, Halstead, Essex	TL774362
Conwy Valley Railway Museum, Old Goods Yard, Betws-y-coed, Gwynedd	SH796565
Dawlish Warren Camp Site, Dawlish Warren, Devon	SX979785
Dean Forest Railway, Norchard Steam Centre, Lydney, Gloucestershire	SO629044
Derwent Valley Light Railway, Yorkshire Museum of Farming, Murton, York, N. Yorks.	SE651537
Didcot Railway Centre (Great Western Society), Didcot, Oxfordshire	SU524906
Dunkleys Restaurant, Castle Ashby Station, Cogenhoe, Northamptonshire	SP859617
East Anglian Railway Museum, Chappel and Wakes Colne Station, Essex	TL898289
East Kent Light Railway, Shepherdswell, Kent	TR258483
East Lancashire Railway, Bolton Street Station, Bury, Greater Manchester	SD803109
East Somerset Railway, Cranmore Railway Station, Shepton Mallet, Somerset	ST664429
Embsay Steam Railway, Embsay Station, Embsay, Skipton, North Yorkshire	SE007533
Fencote Old Station, Hatfield, near Leominster, Herefordshire	SO601589
Foxfield Light Railway, Blythe Bridge, Stoke-on-Trent, Staffordshire	SJ976446
Fransham Station, Great Fransham, Norfolk (Private Site)	TF888135
Glasgow Museum of Transport, Kelvin Hall, Coplawhill, Glasgow, Strathclyde	NS581632
Gloucestershire-Warwickshire Railway, Toddington Station, Gloucestershire	SP020323
Great Bower Farm, Molash, Nr. Challock, Kent (Private Site)	TR033529
Great Central Railway (Southern Division), Appletree Industrial Estate, Chipping Warden, Northamptonshire (Private Site)	SP494494
Great Central Railway, Loughborough Central Station, Leicestershire	SK543194
Great Scottish & Western Railway Company, Euston Downside CARMD (Private Site)	TQ291832
Great Western Museum, Coleford, Gloucestershire	SO576105
Greater Manchester Museum of Science & Industry, Liverpool Road Station, Manchester, Greater Manchester	SJ831978
Grimsby & Louth Railway, Lugborough Station, Lugborough, Lincolnshire	TF308961
Gwili Railway Company, Bronwydd Arms Station, Carmarthen, Dyfed	SN417236
Hayling Island Railway Society, Pepes Boat Yard, Mill Rythe Quay, Mill Rythe Lane, Hayling Island, Hampshire	SU726013

Holme Trading Estate, Holme-on-Spalding Moor, East Yorkshire (Private Site)	SE829359
Horsebridge Station, Kings Sombre, Hampshire (Private Site)	SU344304
Ian Allan Ltd., Terminal House, Shepperton, Middlesex	TQ081675
Ilderton Station House Cafe and Restaurant, Ilderton Station, Ilderton, Northumberland	NU019236
Isle of Wight Steam Railway, Haven Street Station, Isle of Wight	SZ556898
Keighley & Worth Valley Railway, Haworth Station, Haworth, Keighley, W. Yorks.	SE034371
Kent & East Sussex Railway, Tenterden Town Station, Tenterden, Kent	TQ882336
Lakeside Railway, Haverthwaite, Cumbria	SD349843
Leader Foot Viaduct, Leader Foot, Galashiels, Borders	NT573347
Llangollen Railway, Llangollen Station, Llangollen, Clwyd	SJ211423
Mangapp's Farm Railway Museum, Mangapp's Farm, Burnham-on-Crouch, Essex	TQ944980
Marsden Rattler Restaurant, Sea Road, South Shields, Tyne & Wear	NZ377673
Mid-Suffolk Light Railway, Brockford Green, Nr. Stowmarket, Suffolk	TM129659
Middleton Railway, Moor Road, Hunslet, Leeds, West Yorkshire	SE302309
Midland Railway Centre, Butterley Station, Ripley, Derbyshire	SK403520
MoD BAD Kineton, Warwickshire	SP373523
MoD Long Marston Military Railway, Long Marston, Warwickshire (Private Site)	SP153473
Monkwearmouth Station Museum, Monkwearmouth, Sunderland, Tyne & Wear	NZ395578
National Ambulance Museum, Tate & Lyle Building, Harford Bridge, Tavistock, Devon	
National Museum of Wales, Industrial and Maritime Museum, Alexandra Dock Junction Storage Site, Cardiff, South Glamorgan (Private Site)	ST200744
National Museum of Wales, Industrial and Maritime Museum, Broad Street Bus Garage, Broad Street, Barry, South Glamorgan (Private Site)	
National Museum of Wales, Industrial and Maritime Museum, Penarth Flats Storage Site, Penarth Flats, Cardiff, South Glamorgan	ST177729
National Railway Museum, Leeman Road, York, North Yorkshire	SE594519
Nene Valley Railway, Wansford Station, Peterborough, Cambridgeshire	TL093979
Nomix-Chipman, Horsham Goods Yard, Horsham, West Sussex (Private Site)	TQ179313
North Norfolk Railway, 'The Poppy Line', Sheringham Station, Norfolk	TG156430
North Woolwich Old Station Museum, Pier Road, North Woolwich, London	TQ433798
North Yorkshire Moors Railway, Pickering Station, North Yorkshire	NZ828049
Northampton and Lamport Railway, Pitsford & Brampton Station, Pitsford, Northants.	SP736666
Nottingham Heritage Centre, Mereway, Ruddington, Nottinghamshire	SK 571313
Orient Express Restaurant, Elsenham, Cambridgeshire	TL532271
Oswestry Cycle & Railway Museum, Oswestry Station Yard, Oswald Road, Oswestry, Shropshire	SJ294297
Paignton & Dartmouth Railway, Queen's Park Station, Paignton, Devon	SX889606
Peak Railway, 'Peak Rail', Darley Dale Station, Derbyshire	SK273626
Pontypool & Blaenavon Railway, Furnoe Sidings, Big Pit, Blaenavon, Gwent	SO237093
Pullman Lodge Hotel and Restaurant, Seaburn, Sunderland, Tyne & Wear	NZ406595
Rail and Marine Engineering Ltd, Thingley Junction, Chippenham, Wiltshire	ST901708
Railcare, Wolverton Works, Wolverton, Milton Keynes, Buckinghamshire (Private Site)	SP812413
Ravenglass and Eskdale Railway, Ravenglass, Cumbria	SO086967
Rother Valley Railway, Robertsbridge Station Yard, Robertsbridge, East Sussex	TQ734236
Rowden Mill Station, Rowden Mill, Near Bromyard, Hereford and Worcestershire (Private Site)	SO627565
Rutland Railway Museum, Cottesmore Iron Ore Mines Sidings, Cottesmore, Oakham, Leicestershire	SK887137
Sail and Steam Engineering Ltd., The Old Shipyard, Brightlingsea, Essex (Private Site)	TM689163
Scottish Industrial Railway Centre, Minnivy Colliery, Dalmellington, Strathclyde	NS475073
Severn Valley Railway, The Railway Station, Bewdley, Hereford & Worcestershire	SO715926
Somerset & Avon Railway, Radstock, Somerset	ST689549
South Devon Railway, 'The Primrose Line', Buckfastleigh Station, Buckfastleigh, Devon	SX747633
Southall Railway Centre, Old Southall Diesel Depot, Southall, Middlesex	TQ131798
Spa Valley Railway, Tunbridge Wells West Station, Tunbridge Wells, Kent	TQ542346
St. Leonards Railway Engineering, St. Leonards Depot, Hastings, East Sussex (Private Site)	TQ778086
Steamport Railway Museum, Derby Road, Southport, Merseyside	SD341170
Steamtown Railway Centre, Carnforth, Lancashire	SD496708
Stephenson Railway Museum, Middle Engine Lane, West Chirton, North Tyneside, Tyne & Wear	NZ323693
Strathspey Railway, The Station, Boat of Garten, Inverness-shire	NH898131
Swanage Railway, 'The Purbeck Line', Swanage Railway Station, Swanage, Dorset	SZ028789

Swansea Vale Railway, Llansamlet, Swansea, West Glamorgan	SS660928
Swindon & Cricklade Railway, Blunsden Station, Swindon, Wiltshire	SU110897
Swindon L. C. & W Works Ltd, Old No. 20 Shop, Swindon Works, Swindon, Wiltshire (Private Site)	SU140846
Tanfield Railway, Marley Hill Engine Shed, Sunniside, Tyne & Wear	NZ207573
Telford Railway Centre, Old Locomotive Shed, Horsehay, Telford, Shropshire	SJ675073
The Old Marazion Station Holiday Centre, Marazion, Cornwall	SW505312
The Spot Gate, Mier Heath, Hilderstone, Staffordshire	SJ944368
Tintern Parva Station Museum, Tintern Parva, Gwent	SO537004
Titley Junction Station, Near Kington, Hereford & Worcester (Private Site)	SO329581
Tonbridge Model Engineering Society, Brightfriars Meadow, Tonbridge, Kent	TQ588467
Venice-Simplon Orient Express, Sea Containers Ltd, Stewarts Lane T&RSMD, Battersea, London (Private Site)	TQ257798
Wales Railway Centre, Butetown Historic Railway Society Ltd, Bute Road, ButeTown, Cardiff, South Glamorgan, South Wales	ST192749
Watercress Line, New Alresford Station, New Alresford, Hampshire	SU588325
Wessex Traincare Ltd, Eastleigh Works, Eastleigh, Hampshire (Private Site)	SU457185
West Bay Visitor Information Centre, West Bay, near Bridport, Dorset	SY466904
West Somerset Railway, The Railway Station, Minehead, Somerset	SS975463
Ystywth Valley Railway, Llanilar, Aberystywth, Dyfed	